THE BECHTEL STORY

S. D. Bechtel Jr.   *S. D. Bechtel*

The Bechtel Story

SEVENTY YEARS OF ACCOMPLISHMENT
IN ENGINEERING AND CONSTRUCTION

By Robert L. Ingram

SAN FRANCISCO, CALIFORNIA

APRIL, 1968

Contents

Foreword

The scientist, the engineer, and the builder have had a strong hand in raising man's ability to satisfy his physical needs and attain more of his material goals. These three, by the interplay of their efforts, are profoundly changing living standards in a large part of the world.

The scientist mans the front line of research.

The engineer, his practical-minded colleague, adapts the scientist's discoveries to many uses, applying triumphs of the laboratory to important products and facilities that affect the lives of millions.

The builder transforms the engineer's concepts and designs into operating plants, transportation systems, natural resources developments and the countless other physical structures of modern civilization.

This process is particularly apparent in the heavy construction industry where the engineer and the builder work closely together. As an outgrowth of recent scientific advances, construction projects have become increasingly large and complicated. To better meet today's sophisticated demands the working partnership of designer and builder in a number of cases has evolved into a single entity, the engineer-constructor, who performs in both these capacities.

Bechtel is such an organization. It has carried the complete responsibility concept to a high point of development and has achieved wide diversification in the scope and geography of its operations.

This engineer-constructor's activities in the years following mid-century are rich in materials for a story that invites telling, both on its own merits and as part of the larger role of private initiative in making this period a time of unprecedented accomplishment and prosperity.

In the company's continuing progress the 1950's were especially significant for still another reason. That period represented the culmination of more than 40 years of service and 25 years of policy direction and senior management by the family's second generation leader, Stephen D. Bechtel. For when the 1960's began he was succeeded in the presidency by Stephen Jr., marking the start of a new era.

W. A. Bechtel

CHAPTER ONE

The First Fifty Years

Shortly before the turn of the century, in a world which had changed less in 2000 years than it would in the next seventy, a young midwest rancher hired out with his mules to work a stretch of railroad grade in Indian Territory, now Oklahoma.

1898: How It Began — W. A. Bechtel

On that day a business was born, for once the young man had tasted the pride in achievement that accompanies the sweat and grime of heavy construction, he knew he had found his life work. The twenty-six-year-old builder and his growing family soon moved westward, following the rails and on his own account, laying the groundwork for the business organization to come. In the succeeding 70 years his company would achieve remarkable continuity under the direction of three chief executives — himself, W. A. Bechtel, its founder; his son, Stephen D.; and his grandson Stephen D. Jr.

Of these, the first two generations divided the span from 1898 through 1960. W. A. Bechtel served as president until his death in the 1930's and S. D. Bechtel thereafter until 1960 when, as chairman of the board, he relinquished the presidency upon S. D. Bechtel Jr.'s election to that office and the start of the company's present era under third generation leadership.

Arthur V. Bechtel

From almost the start of his activities W. A. Bechtel had a trusted colleague at his side, his younger brother Arthur. Art Bechtel learned heavy construction in the field, starting while still in his teens. His active lifetime was concurrent with the great change in construction equipment from primitive tools energized by men and animals to the early versions of today's efficient power machines. By perceptive observation

I

and practical suggestions he contributed to numerous improvements in methods and equipment, and in many other ways to the success of the family business. He remained on its Board until less than two years before his death in 1946.

The Sons

For three decades W. A. Bechtel made railroad construction his main concern, even after 1919-'24 when, in succession, his sons Warren, Stephen, and Kenneth came into the business. Somewhat earlier W. A. — as his cronies called him — had taken part in the realignment of Southern Pacific's Overland Route and the building of other parts of that system, and in the original construction of the Western Pacific and the Northwestern Pacific. Subsequently he branched out to build highways, water systems and other public works.

Earle G. Lloyd, Frank C. Sewell

Two early employees, Earle Lloyd and Frank Sewell, were instrumental in the progress of the business. Earle Lloyd, ten years W. A. Bechtel's junior, joined the firm in 1910. A young insurance man from Nebraska, he came in to look after the company's growing insurance requirements and became its principal administrator as well. A close and warm friendship developed and for years he was W. A.'s right hand man. Then in 1920, W. A. Bechtel, together with another contractor, Arch Borland, founded the predecessor organization to Industrial Indemnity Company to meet the employers' liability needs of California contractors. Earle Lloyd took over its management.

Participating as a director in the insurance firm was a third contractor, Henry J. Kaiser, whom W. A. had long held in high regard as a business associate. A close friendship between the families has continued through succeeding generations.

In 1931 Kenneth Bechtel was elected president of the insurance firm and today, as chairman, remains its chief executive. Earle Lloyd served as its secretary-treasurer and a director until his retirement in 1947. He passed away in 1966.

Frank Sewell joined W. A. Bechtel in 1914 during the building of the Northwestern Pacific Railroad's extension from Willits to Ukiah,

Arthur V. Bechtel joined his brother on the railroad jobs at an early age and became an expert on construction methods. Equipment was always a prime interest with him, like this steam shovel, at work in the 1920's double-tracking railroad mainline over the California Sierra.

California. He broke in under Lloyd as an "office man — even then a necessary evil on construction jobs," Sewell used to say. He worked with the Bechtels for more than 30 years, most of that time as a ranking administrative and accounting officer, serving as assistant to Kenneth Bechtel during Kenneth's years as the company's financial executive.

As they grew up, the three Bechtel boys spent increasing amounts of time out on their father's projects, becoming active to the point of taking subcontracts for small jobs, such as culverts. It was his way of teaching self-reliance and responsibility, and of giving the boys a real taste of construction. This work brought them into close contact with Art Bechtel, Earle Lloyd and Frank Sewell, to whom they became closely attached. Frank, particularly, became their champion and confidant. When Art died in 1946 and Frank in the following year, a strong link was broken with the well-remembered railroad construction camps and the rugged days when horsepower literally meant horses or mules. From this background of lifelong friendships, hard physical work and homely truths learned out on the jobs, evolved many of the business philosophies that still guide the Bechtel organization.

Alice Bechtel

At about the time the older boys were being given their first chores on the railroad jobs during school vacations, a daughter was born to the W. A. Bechtels. Named Alice Elizabeth, she — like her niece Barbara a generation later — grew up in a family whose lively enthusiasm for construction became a part of daily life. The Bechtels numbered among their friends many accomplished people in the professional and business world and frequently entertained them at home. As a result, Alice was rather knowledgeable about engineering, construction and industry in general and thus became an interested — if unofficial — member of the family business team.

W. A. Bechtel Co.

In 1925, with capacity augmented by the sons' participation, the business was incorporated as W. A. Bechtel Co., and operations were further expanded. Warren, by now well versed in railroad construction, supervised the building of Bowman Dam in Nevada County, California,

4

W. A. Bechtel with sons Stephen, Kenneth and Warren Jr. during construction of Southern Pacific's Natron Cut-Off in Oregon, 1924.

Bottom dump wagons were basic heavy construction equipment in Bechtel's early years.

When winter snows isolated the Bowman Dam job in 1925, emergency supplies were mailed in parcel post packages and delivered by dog sled.

where he was joined by Kenneth, who took charge of the grouting.

Two fields of construction entered in that period, hydroelectric power and oil and natural gas pipelines, were to become important permanent types of work for the company. Bechtel's first pipeline, laid in California, proved a significant step in the firm's progress because it initiated what was to become a major policy — gearing the organization to the construction needs of certain vigorous industries chosen for their strong, long-term growth potential.

During the 1930's Bechtel's volume in pipelines increased steadily. But the depression was on and there was a big drop in railroad jobs so the company turned its attention to public works. Two projects in particular were milestones in its development.

1931-'36: Hoover Dam

The first of these was Hoover Dam on the Colorado River, also known as Boulder Dam, built in an outstanding performance by Six Companies Inc., in which Bechtel and Kaiser interests actively took part. Bechtel-Kaiser-Warren Company was the medium; its participants included Bechtel, Kaiser, and Warren Bros., a Boston firm.

The Bechtels had important roles. W. A. was elected president of Six Companies in 1931 and served until his death in 1933. His son, Steve, was first vice president and a member of the four-man Executive Committee, of which Henry Kaiser was chairman. As administrative director, Steve had charge of administration, purchasing and transportation.

Lasting associations were formed on the Hoover Dam project. W. E. Waste came into the organization to direct purchasing and within a short time assumed an important place in Bechtel management. J. Perry Yates, who was office engineer for Six Companies, subsequently became a major contributor to Bechtel success.

In its day Hoover Dam was by far the largest construction job ever undertaken anywhere as a prime contract, and even by present standards ranks among the most formidable. Its completion in under five years, two years ahead of schedule, demonstrated that its builders would make their marks in the construction world. Hoover's graduates included Stephen and Kenneth Bechtel; Henry and Edgar Kaiser, and Clay Bedford of the Kaiser organization; H. W. Morrison of Morrison-Knudsen;

Hoover Dam under construction by Six Companies Inc., August 31, 1934.

Congratulations poured into W. A. Bechtel's office after his election as national president of Associated General Contractors. With him on the happy occasion were E. S. Burney of Nevada Construction Co. (left) and Bechtel veteran Earle Lloyd.

Six Companies and U.S. Bureau of Reclamation officials at Hoover Dam, 1932. From left: H. J. Lawler, W. R. Young, Chas. A. Shea, E. O. Wattis, Dr. Elwood Mead, Frank Crowe, R. F. Walter and W. A. Bechtel.

and Gil Shea of J. F. Shea Co., Inc., all subsequently among the industry's greatest leaders.

1933-'36: San Francisco-Oakland Bay Bridge

The second prominent job of the 1930's in which Bechtel and Kaiser participated was construction of the San Francisco-Oakland Bay Bridge, this time as a member of Bridge Builders, Inc. That joint venture completed two important contracts on the project — one for the pier foundations of the East Bay crossing and the other for painting the entire eight-mile bridge.

B. M. Eubanks

In 1937 Alice Bechtel married Brantley M. Eubanks, a young veteran of both the dam and bridge jobs. He had joined the firm some years earlier in field engineering at Hoover Dam, shortly after graduating from the University of California. Subsequently he handled cost analysis on the Bay Bridge work, and remained with the Bechtel organization for a number of years thereafter before finding his real field in the investment business.

Changing Emphasis, Public to Private Work

Completion of Hoover Dam and the Bay Bridge marked Bechtel's peak in large joint ventures and in civic engineering-type construction for government bodies. In the late 1930's, Henry Kaiser and his colleagues went their way into manufacturing — in cement, steel and later, aluminum — whereas the Bechtels remained in engineering and construction.

These large public works were advantageous to the contractors in enabling them to strengthen their organizations and financial resources. But while the public jobs were still in full swing Steve Bechtel set about to increase the company's services to industry. His plans began to produce results shortly after his brothers elected him president of the company in the mid-1930's. In the next several years this change from public to private work would alter the basic character of the organization.

Already the first phase of Bechtel's development had ended. During its initial thirty-odd years the business had been largely the successful outgrowth of one man's thinking and work, a courageous pioneering effort in construction by W. A. Bechtel, virtually confined to the far western part of the United States.

Now the pace was quickening. With wider horizons and a growing workload, Steve and his brothers brought in others, choosing carefully with an eye to their varied experience and future management capabilities. Many of these men were to remain for lifetime careers, helping to shape the enterprise and rising to positions of major importance.

Second Generation Leadership — S. D. Bechtel

The next stage in the evolution of the business was the product of the family's second generation under Steve's direction, aided by their colleagues. As it always has been, Bechtel was an organization of young men, particularly at this time. Most of its leaders were still in their thirties, some in their twenties, only one over fifty.

In upper management the two veterans of the Hoover Dam project, Bill Waste and Perry Yates, were to have very important places in the executive structure during the next thirty years.

In the mid-1930's Waste was elected secretary of W. A. Bechtel Co. Later, with senior administrative responsibilities, he became a ranking officer of Bechtel Corporation and a major participant in policy making.

Yates took a leading part in Bechtel-McCone's activities, commencing with the formation of that company in 1937. In the consolidated operation after 1945, many of Bechtel's most important fields of work were inaugurated and brought to vigorous activity under his direction.

Several men, not active with the company in recent years, joined Bechtel in the 1930's and were influential in its development. Of particular importance in this respect were George S. Colley Jr., V. G. Hindmarsh, Van W. Rosendahl and John A. McCone.

Like the Bechtels, whom he joined in 1932, George S. Colley Jr. was a second generation builder. When elected vice president of W. A. Bechtel Co. in 1935 he was the first person outside the family to become a company officer. He supervised construction of the earliest Bechtel overseas project — a pipeline in Venezuela — and remained active on the international side of the business.

A senior in experience when he joined the firm in 1934, V. G.

"Heinie" Hindmarsh had charge of refinery and chemical activities for many years. His knowledge and judgment were broadly utilized at top level. "Heinie" was a real pioneer. His 60 years in the industry spanned the whole modern era of construction.

Van Rosendahl came into the organization in 1939. A key executive during 15 years with the company, he was principal officer on the difficult wartime Canol sub-Arctic pipeline and refinery project and thereafter was responsible for management of pipeline operations and international activities.

Refineries and Chemical Plants

During construction at Hoover Dam, John McCone and Steve Bechtel renewed a friendship formed at college. As a steel company officer, McCone was a leading supplier to the big project. At that time Steve's forward planning was closely linked with energy in general and oil in particular. When he decided in 1937 to form a new organization to engineer and build refineries and chemical plants, he invited McCone to become a partner and its managing head.

Bechtel-McCone was launched in 1937 and for a period of time engineer Ralph M. Parsons participated as a principal. This business grew rapidly into a major firm in its type of work. Later, Bechtel-McCone diversified to successfully handle large assignments in support of the war effort. Following consolidation of all Bechtel operations at the war's end, McCone turned to the management of his own interests and began a new career of distinguished service to government.

More Young Men Came In

A. J. Orselli joined Bechtel in 1933 as a young engineer in his twenties. Over the years at home and abroad his assignments have been among the most diversified in the entire organization.

In 1934, when most of the volume was in public work, E. J. Garbarini and Clark Rankin were added to the force on a large highway tunnel project. Each man advanced steadily, acquiring senior stature.

Entry into the engineering and construction of processing facilities brought Charles T. Draney into the organization in 1937. A chemical and petroleum engineer, he soon addressed himself to the development of new business in these specialties with marked success. With passing time his responsibilities were widened.

John Merryman came with the firm in 1939, two years after getting his engineering degree from the United States Naval Academy. After successfully handling heavy project duties during and after the war, he moved up to take part in Bechtel's nuclear power work.

Another whose Bechtel service dated from 1939 was Edward E. Dorresten. An experienced engineer when he joined Bechtel-McCone as manager of that company's San Francisco office, he became manager of engineering and subsequently — in 1951 — a vice president of Bechtel Corporation. He specialized in the refinery and chemical field, serving as assistant to Heinie Hindmarsh, until shortly before Dorresten's untimely death in the summer of 1955.

In the 1930's and early 1940's the two companies — W. A. Bechtel Co. in San Francisco and Bechtel-McCone in Los Angeles — operated independently but in close communication with each other. The older firm undertook a wide range of project types, the younger concentrated on petroleum refineries and chemical plants.

Engineering and the Turn-Key Project

The advent of Bechtel-McCone marked an important step in Bechtel's development, for it was active in fields which required heavy engineering capabilities. Subsequently the emphasis gradually shifted in the older company as well, from construction with engineering overtones, to a balanced engineering and construction activity. Interest in energy inevitably led to work in electric power for the utilities.

By 1940 the Bechtel companies were beginning to acquire the characteristics of the comprehensive organization Steve Bechtel envisioned, one that would be prepared in its chosen fields to render a turn-key service. At the time "turn-key" was a new concept in the construction industry. It meant an all-encompassing service — everything needed for the realization of major projects, including engineering, procurement and construction — under single responsibility.

First Overseas Work

In 1940, also, the business took on a new dimension when operations were extended beyond the North American continent. The earliest work, undertaken in Venezuela with joint venture partners, consisted of an oil pipeline, docks, a jungle-piercing road and telephone lines. Without interruption from that day to this, Bechtel has been active beyond the national borders in lands near and far.

Ray L. Hamilton

Ray L. Hamilton joined the Bechtel organization in 1940 and for the next 18 years was a tower of strength in its pipeline activities. Internationally recognized as an authority on pipeline economics and engineering, as the years advanced he had important roles in the planning and construction of such major pipelines as the Trans-Arabian, Super Inch, Trans Mountain, Westcoast Transmission and Lakehead Extension projects. He was elected to a Bechtel Corporation vice presidency in 1954. When death closed his highly productive career in 1958, Ray Hamilton left many enduring monuments in the form of great pipeline systems to which he contributed so much of his knowledge, judgment and wisdom.

World War II — National Defense

War had broken out in Europe in 1939. Before long it was apparent that involvement of the United States was probable. Like others, Bechtel management was aware of the implications for the construction industry.

Work for the naval and military forces got under way in 1940 as joint ventures with other contractors. For the United States, war was more than a year away but Bechtel was occupied in preparing for it. Steve was constantly on the move as the organization's chief executive. The company staffed and manned defense-supported operations at such widely separated locations as the Philippines, Alaska, and Bahrain.

The first of these, undertaken as a member of Contractors Pacific Naval Air Bases, a joint venture in which George Colley sponsored the Bechtel participation, involved modernizing the Navy's major installations at Cavite and Sangley Point. Work started in April, 1941, went ahead at top speed, but by December Japanese air strikes had ended activity at both locations. The construction crews continued to build air fields and ammunition dumps in the mountains. Soon, however, the

13

Japanese invaded. Colley and his wife courageously struck out for Australia in a small boat, were captured and spent the rest of the war in a prison camp on Borneo.

At that time Warren Bechtel had charge of many of the firm's major construction activities, including those for the mining industry. As defense responsibilities, Warren's team literally dug in, building open pit mines and processing plants in the Southwest to increase the nation's short supply of copper. Three big copper projects, built in outstanding performances, were a fitting climax to his quarter century of service.

John M. Rogers, a mining engineer, joined the firm in 1941 and soon was active on one of the copper projects. Rogers later advanced to a senior vice presidency and became a director. As the chief officer for international operations, he managed a wide variety of overseas activities, until his retirement in 1955.

Kenneth Bechtel became the family's Number One shipbuilder. Kenneth's main concern was Marinship Corporation at Sausalito, California. There as president and with Bill Waste as general manager, he directed an operation that won the Government's highest commendation for its accomplishments.

Plenty of Variety

Shipyards and ships, naval bases, the Army's main western port, powder plants, oil refineries, a pioneering 1600-mile oil and products pipeline system through unmapped northern wilderness conceived by the U. S. Army engineers and called the Canol Project, portions of the U. S. "Big Inch" pipeline, and a large military aircraft modification center at Birmingham, Alabama — built and operated — were among the war responsibilities Bechtel undertook, alone or in joint ventures.

Biggest of these operations were two shipyards, the aforementioned Marinship located on San Francisco Bay and California Shipbuilding Corporation ("Calship") in Los Angeles harbor, which preceded Marinship by a year and three months. Calship, one of the largest shipyards in the country, was built and operated under Bechtel-McCone sponsorship, with John McCone as president and Steve Bechtel as board chairman. The two shipyards delivered a combined total of 560 ships — Liberties, Victories, and the more complex T-2 tankers and Navy oilers.

California Shipbuilding Corporation delivered 4.8 million deadweight tons of merchant ships representing nearly 10 per cent of the total U.S. Maritime Commission war emergency program.

New Associates

Closely associated with management during the war years and thereafter were two members of outside firms, John L. Simpson and Robert L. Bridges. Both became directors of Bechtel Corporation. Simpson, a veteran international banker, served as financial counsellor in the 1940's and came into the firm full time in the early 1950's as chairman of the Finance Committee, continuing in that capacity until his retirement in 1961. He has been valued as highly for his judgment and personal qualities as for his expertise in international finance.

Bridges, a partner in the legal firm that serves as the company's counsel, has devoted most of his time to Bechtel as a principal adviser, contributing greatly in establishing legal and corporate policy.

A War Bonus — Potential Executives

Wartime responsibilities vastly expanded Bechtel's activities and manpower. Steve has said, "we were stretched so taut that every man was called on to do more than he thought possible and many men more than met the challenge. They really grew up under these pressures. Out of the war operations our company drew much of its future leadership."

He had in mind men like John R. Kiely, a department manager at Calship; J. W. Komes, who started as assistant superintendent during Calship's construction; I. R. Caraco, a principal engineer at Calship; John F. O'Connell, labor coordinator at Marinship; R. D. Grammater, assistant administrative manager on Canol; Eugene Lippa, field engineer on wartime refinery projects and J. K. Doolan, Calship's general manager. All moved steadily up into senior responsibilities by different routes, and eventually to directorships on Bechtel Corporation's Board. Except for Doolan, who retired from active to consulting status, this group constitutes a substantial part of today's top management.

John Kiely's upward path has been through the power and industrial branches of the company, where he has worked closely with Perry Yates.

When Calship closed, Jerry Komes joined Bechtel's Industrial Division. Subsequently, when the operating divisions were realigned, Komes took a major role in the international work.

Ike Caraco moved from Calship to the Vernon office on Southern California Edison's frequency change program in 1945. Later he was

Warren, Stephen and Kenneth Bechtel at the height of their war production and construction responsibilities.

John A. McCone and S. D. Bechtel at Calship. McCone was Calship's president and executive sponsor, Bechtel its board chairman.

A Six Companies reunion at Marinship —Kenneth and Steve Bechtel with Felix Kahn, Edgar and Henry Kaiser.

given design responsibilities on certain power projects.

John O'Connell demonstrated his talent for handling labor and industrial relations so well at Marinship that at war's end he was put in charge of these activities for Bechtel Corporation. His abilities led to still greater responsibilities as time passed.

Through education and background, Rudy Grammater—an attorney and certified public accountant—prepared for duty in the company's accounting and administrative sectors. He served overseas and later worked directly under John Simpson on major finance and tax matters.

Not long after getting his engineering degree at the University of Idaho, Gene Lippa came into the organization on the refinery construction side, acquiring experience on the job and steadily advancing. With growth of the foreign workload he moved into that branch of operations.

Complementing these men were others drawn from the ranks of the war oriented enterprises. Occupying key positions in later years were Martin Akeyson, Glenn E. Buchanan, Donald R. Ferguson, James M. Leaver, Jake Lindenbaum, Fred W. Meyer, J. S. Sides, K. O. Taylor, Porter E. Thompson and Harry F. Waste.

In addition to providing these future officers, the defense activities first brought another young man into the fold. Stephen D. Bechtel Jr. commenced his career in engineering-construction on survey parties and in other work on wartime projects during the school vacations of 1941 and 1942. There in the field he got the first true understanding of construction that only direct contact can give.

1945: Resources Consolidated

When the whistles blew on August 14, 1945 announcing Japan's surrender they brought an end to construction for war. But major allied successes and Germany's capitulation had clearly forecast the coming of peace. By spring Bechtel's management had its conversion plans well in mind. In September a new entity, which today is Bechtel Corporation, was incorporated and brought together the functions performed by the separate organizations, W. A. Bechtel Co., and Bechtel-McCone.

At this time Warren and Kenneth Bechtel and John McCone retired from active participation in the business, although several years later Kenneth returned as a director and counsellor.

Warren, eldest of the brothers, applied himself to his personal interests. Kenneth Bechtel's responsibilities, as president of Industrial Indemnity Company, required his complete attention. John McCone, before long, was in Washington on the first of several important public service assignments for the Federal Government. All had played very important parts in the Bechtel organization's upbuilding.

Peace — a Rapid Transition

American industry was off to a fast postwar start, with engineering and construction in great demand. Bechtel received substantial contracts. Many were for turn-key projects. The company promply designed and built plants to manufacture food, soap, steel products, paper, glass fiber and other items. It was beginning to achieve the diversification that would be one of its most important characteristics in later years. Some war projects, like two oil refineries in the Middle East, were forerunners of very large peacetime developments.

Pipeline construction, brisk during the war, became even more active. On one of the domestic pipeline projects of 1948, Stephen D. Bechtel Jr. entered the company's employ full time.

He had earned his master's degree in Business Administration at Stanford in 1948, completing a stiff two years of work in 18 months and paralleling his excellent earlier performance at the University of Colorado and Purdue University, where he received his bachelor's degree in civil engineering. Meanwhile he had married — the young lady was Elizabeth "Betty" Hogan — and while at Stanford eldest daughter Shana had been born. Likewise, Steve Jr. had served three years in the Marine Corps and received his lieutenant's commission.

When his work with the company began, Steve's start was out on the jobs — in the Midwest, Southwest, Pacific Coast and Canada.

Activities Expanded

During the late 1940's three significant trends emerged in the company's growth pattern. First, Bechtel greatly increased its overseas volume, mainly by becoming the largest engineer-constructor of oil transportation and processing facilities in the Middle East. Second, a Canadian company was set up and staffed, and commitments were received for the development of some of that country's abundant natural resources. Third, power capabilities and organization were expanded, substantially raising Bechtel's service output for the electric utility industry.

These moves solidified the company's position in important areas of the world and in classes of work which thereafter represented major parts of its business. Another result was the arrival of more people with good executive potential, such as James N. Landis and William H. Ness. These two men, both experienced engineers, assumed high-level responsibilities in power business development and management.

The Toronto-based activities of Canadian Bechtel Limited were pioneered and managed for over 15 years by Sidney M. Blair. Canadian by birth, he was a well-known international petroleum engineer and executive when he joined the organization in 1949. His appointment initiated a policy, strictly observed, of Canadian executive direction for Canadian activities.

The First Half Century

In more than 50 years of existence the Bechtel enterprise had developed from a business initially built around one man, W. A. Bechtel, into a ranking engineering and construction organization handling a diversity of work at home and overseas.

Along the way it had come through the long depression of the 1930's gaining strength, it had fully met war's heavy demands and had just finished five busy years of post-war service to industry.

These were sizable achievements. Before long, however, there would be far greater successes. There also would be problems and changes. The next decade would bring the realization, above all, that when an organization has sufficient will and vigor and management capability there is no ceiling on its potential for accomplishment.

CHAPTER TWO

Bechtel at Mid-Century

Mid-century 1950 was the year when the Cold War blazed hot in Korea, bringing the first battles ever fought between jet planes, a time when heads of state of the major powers were Harry S. Truman, Josef Stalin, and Clement Attlee. The NATO alliance celebrated its first anniversary but seven years were to pass before formation of the European Common Market. Computers were little more than a promise as far as their use in business was concerned and atomic power was still in the laboratory.

1950's: A Growth Decade, Worldwide

As for the decade ahead which, in a Bechtel frame of reference will be the concern of the next several chapters, tremendous changes were in store. The U. S. Gross National Product grew from the area of $285 billions in 1950 to over $480 billions in 1959, a 70 per cent rise, while the consumer price index climbed 20 per cent, showing that prosperity was mostly solid and not primarily the result of inflation. There was no serious depression in the entire period, although there were setbacks in 1954 after the Korean War and again in 1957-'58.

Canada did even better, virtually doubling its national product. Immense natural resources were opened — iron and copper ore deposits in the northwest, and oil and natural gas in the west.

Most of the western-aligned countries were freeing themselves from the effects of war and starting to revitalize their economies with the help of the Marshall Plan together with other sources of American money, materials and management. To serve these emerging foreign markets, especially in Europe and the Pacific, American firms built production facilities overseas. Total private U. S. investment in foreign countries jumped from $19 billions in 1950 to $50 billions in 1960.

Construction enjoyed healthy growth at home and abroad. In the United States the construction industry's annual volume of new work rose from $33 billions at the beginning of the decade to $55 billions in 1959. Closer to Bechtel's interest, domestic expenditures for new plant and equipment went up from $20.5 billions (1950) to $32.6 billions (1959), a full 60 per cent increase in the annual rate.

In this healthful climate the company's business grew and flourished. Against a background of unprecedented facilities expansion involving the great names of private enterprise Bechtel was active, anticipating needs and enlarging its capabilities to implement industry's growth program. Many of these firms were clients of long standing.

Bechtel's Activity Level

In 1950 Bechtel's "level of effort," that combination of vital statistics by which top managment measures the state of the business, was at a peacetime high with respect to the past. Most significant, backlog was growing fast.

In his 1950 holiday message to employees, S. D. Bechtel spoke of the increase in demand and of the problems to be met in expanding a technical organization. Said he:

"The worldwide developments now in the making are resulting in substantial requirements for new projects. Already we have been called upon to assume added responsibilities and volume.

"These programs will call for additional competent, experienced engineering, construction and administrative personnel. We are all proud of the quality and character of those who constitute our organization and, as our expansion takes place, it is important that we preserve our traditional high standards."

Management — Present and Future

At this time the business was 52 years old. Management was middle aged at the top with many outstanding younger men in the wings, ready for heavier responsibilities. When opportunities arose, as they would in this decade, these younger men would furnish capable management for a greatly expanded operation. Under their direction, hundreds of new people would be hired, assimilated, trained in Bechtel ways and molded into a cohesive team. The company once again would provide its leadership principally from within, so effectively that its newer, larger organization would maintain its excellent performance standards and characteristics — a privately owned company managed by its owners.

The Board of Directors at mid-century consisted of S. D. Bechtel, president; W. E. Waste, J. P. Yates, V. W. Rosendahl, G. S. Colley Jr., J. K. Doolan, V. G. Hindmarsh and C. S. Snodgrass, vice presidents; G. E. Walling, treasurer; K. K. Bechtel, R. L. Bridges, J. L. Simpson, John Byrne and John Rogers, directors. Their ages ranged from 40 to 53, with one director 58 and one over 60.

The next generation of executives, in their thirties and forties, were then in upper and middle management, or in charge of projects.

S. D. Bechtel Jr. was nearing the end of several years of diversified assignments in the field. In the spring and summer of 1950 Steve Jr., with his wife Betty and their two small children, like the senior Steves on earlier construction jobs, was living in a home on wheels. This one was a house trailer on the "Super Inch" pipeline — at 34 inches in diameter the biggest-to-date natural gas trunk line. A little later in the year he served as superintendent on some tricky river crossings in Iowa. Soon he would assume still greater responsibilities on projects in Canada.

John Kiely, whose abilities had earned him a senior position as manager of the Power Division by 1948, was busily advancing that part of the company's activities.

In a situation somewhat parallel to that of Kiely, Jerry Komes — not yet 40 — was manager of Bechtel's Industrial Division, then based in Los Angeles.

With eight years of service now behind him, John O'Connell was compiling an excellent record as manager of Labor Relations and Safety, two sensitive areas with an important bearing on the company's success.

Rudy Grammater was in Saudi Arabia, managing administrative and service support for Bechtel's extensive operations in that part of the world.

Charlie Draney, having changed from engineering to sales some years before when he opened the company's New York office, was at San Francisco headquarters in charge of refinery business development.

Ed Garbarini, as general superintendent, had his 1200-man crew moving ahead at a fast clip on the three-unit Contra Costa Steam Plant near Antioch, California, biggest in Bechtel's power experience to date.

Gene Lippa, another engineer-builder, was superintendent on expansion of the grass-roots Salt Lake Refinery.

Down-to-earth Projects

As these activities indicated, most of the company's work in 1950 was on projects of basic types — nothing exotic or spectacular, or so it might seem in this space age. But even then, improving technologies were changing the old ways and catching the imagination of the engineers. Each new job brought its own stimulating demands and there was anticipation, excitement and high morale in the Bechtel organization. Parenthetically it may be said that with the great technological strides now being made, engineering and construction for heavy industry is becoming less routine every year and will continue to offer great challenges and opportunities.

Then, as now, the company's operations largely revolved around natural resources and energy. Thus, in 1950 the spectrum of Bechtel's work consisted of about a dozen types of projects: oil and natural gas pipelines, marine terminals and piers, oil field support facilities, steam and hydroelectric generating plants, substations, oil refineries, chemical plants, food and industrial plants. These were enough to make the company the most diversified of all engineer-constructors, just as some of the projects of the time were the largest and most important of their kind.

On the domestic scene, 1950 saw the 500-mile 34-inch diameter Super Inch natural gas pipeline completed in California as well as the start of a 400-mile section for a midwestern gas transmission company. In addition to the 300,000-kilowatt Contra Costa power plant, construction was in progress on a 60,000-kilowatt station in Utah. Big Creek 4, a dam and hydroelectric project, was being built by a joint venture in the southern Sierra Nevada. Major refinery installations were under way in Buffalo and Cleveland. Construction started on two western chemical plants, and in Los Angeles a large, highly automated complex for the manufacture of famous-name packaged soaps, detergents and food products was nearing completion.

EBR-1, Precursor of Nuclear Power

Most important of all, but a relatively small project among those that

24

Reviewing progress on the 500-mile "Super Inch" natural gas pipeline—S.D. Bechtel and the pipeline's job engineer, S.D. Bechtel Jr.

Russ Johnson, supervising engineer, and Gene Lippa, superintendent, during expansion of the Salt Lake Refinery.

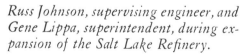

Leaders in early overseas activities were, from left: Earl F. English, George Walling, Van Rosendahl, all of Bechtel, and R. A. "Bob" Conyes, joint venture associate in some of the Middle East work.

then occupied the company's resources, was an Atomic Energy Commission job in rural Idaho. It was one of two performed by Bechtel at the National Reactor Testing Station near Arco, and was called EBR-1, meaning Experimental Breeder Reactor Number 1. It became, in fact, the root of a great revolution in electric power generation that would simmer for nearly a decade and then, in the mid-1960's, break out in a worldwide surge of major nuclear power plants. At Arco, in the Bechtel-constructed facility, history was made in 1951 when, for the first time anywhere, nuclear fission supplied the energy to generate electricity. True, it was only a small amount, just enough to operate some equipment and light some lamp bulbs, but the experiment proved that power generation from this great energy source was technically feasible.

Canada's First Big Oil Pipeline

In 1950 also, another significant step — at least for Bechtel — was the award of a substantial 450-mile section of the Interprovincial pipeline which would eventually link newly developed oil fields in Alberta with a refinery center at Sarnia, Ontario. Initially engineered in part by Bechtel, it was the first truly large Canadian job in peacetime, destined to be the forerunner of the company's extensive activities in the development of Canada's great natural resources.

Bechtel in the Middle East

With completion in 1950 of a full decade of overseas operations, it was apparent that the firm had earned some measure of recognition as a capable international engineer-constructor, particularly in the oil industry. But as yet virtually all of its foreign business was concentrated in the Middle East.

For Aramco, the major concessionaire in Saudi Arabia, the company was expanding the Ras Tanura Refinery, building an oil loading pier, and making oil field installations. In the fall the biggest Arabian job was finished when the 1100-mile Trans-Arabian pipeline system went into operation. It was the greatest overseas pipeline project undertaken up to that time and for many years thereafter.

Better known as Tapline, this project connects the oil producing areas near the Gulf with the Mediterranean Sea at ancient Sidon. The line

One of the world's largest oil refineries—the Ras Tanura plant in Saudi Arabia.

crosses Saudi Arabia, Jordan, Syria, and Lebanon. In its first years of operation Tapline's capacity was 300,000 barrels per day. At this stage of its development the system represented an installed cost approximating $230 millions, all privately financed.

Bechtel's part as joint venture sponsor in the three-year construction program — consisting of 850 miles of trunk and feeder pipelines, four major pumping stations and appurtenances — amounted to 80 per cent of the total project. Working with some 1000 expatriates and a force of 14,000 Arab workers at peak, the organization, under Van Rosendahl at home, George Colley in the field, and Rudy Grammater on administration, accomplished an outstanding feat of supply and construction in excellent time under great difficulties.

Tapline reduced the sea routes to Europe by 3500 miles. There can be no doubt that the vast amount of oil it carried economically across the desert was an important factor in Europe's economic recovery.

Modernizing an Ancient Land

Some of the Saudi Arab oil revenues were invested in public improvements by the King's Government. Bechtel interests planned, engineered, constructed, and managed from concept to completion the facilities in this program, and initially operated many of them. Included were a 100-mile railroad from the interior to the Gulf; a causeway and seven-mile trestle to deepwater; the first large marine terminal on the Red Sea; airports at Riyadh and Jiddah; power plants and water systems; a paved road along the historic Jiddah-Mecca pilgrim trail and other modern projects in that venerable land. In a sense this program, directed by Earl F. English — a senior Bechtel engineering executive — was a prelude to the company's urban planning activities of the 1960's.

Bahrain and Kuwait

To the east, on Bahrain Island, additions were made to a large petroleum refinery, originally built by Bechtel-McCone in 1943-'44. To the north, as work on Tapline phased out, the company prepared to construct the 550-mile IPC oil pipeline through Iraq and Syria. And at the head of the Gulf in the small but important shaikhdom of Kuwait, Bechtel completed a two-year facilities program valued at $40 millions.

Approximately 40 per cent of the Trans-Arabian pipeline is above ground, held in place by ring girders mounted on concrete or pile supports.

Standing beside the final pipe joint to mark completion of Bechtel's 850 miles of pipeline were A. N. Horne, left, Tapline vice president; Roy Middleton, Bechtel superintendent; S. D. Bechtel, and George S. Colley Jr.

Happy birthday: Steve's 50th was celebrated in Dhahran, Saudi Arabia, with his wife, Laura, and George Colley.

Construction of the IPC Pipeline through Iraq and Syria increased Western Europe's oil supply by over 300,000 barrels daily.

S. D. Bechtel congratulates R. L. Bowman, Pipeline Division construction manager, on completion of the "Super Inch" pipeline in California.

One of its main features — the world's largest oil pier — had gone into operation, servicing as many as eight tankers simultaneously and handling up to 1.2 million barrels of oil in 24 hours.

World Travelers

As on domestic projects, Bechtel's seniors responsible for foreign operations were regular visitors at overseas offices and job sites. Leading the way were the company's chief executive and his gracious wife, Laura. All through this period they were on the road as much as half of the time, logging 50,000 miles or more a year.

In a 1955 profile of Steve, Fortune magazine observed that in 32 years of marriage "and traipsing around the world Laura Bechtel has become knowledgeable about the business and inured to this way of life."

"Steve," the magazine added, "is a defender of 'wives of management'; Bechtel Corp. gladly bears their traveling expenses."

Takeoff for a Busy Decade

So it was at mid-century. Heavily occupied at home and abroad with the largest number of major projects in any year of its peacetime history, the Bechtel organization was at work meeting schedules, assuming new responsibilities, building capabilities and planning ahead, as its president said at the time, for a future that held many bright opportunities.

31

North pier of Kuwait marine terminal at Mina al Ahmadi.

With eight berths the Kuwait jetty set the world pace for tanker loading capacity.

CHAPTER THREE

The Bechtel Business Family:

ITS PHILOSOPHIES AND TRADITIONS

As with other successful enterprises and to a greater extent than most, the Bechtel organization has acquired a unique reputation over the past 70 years within the framework of some strongly held points of view on the part of its top management. For one thing the company, for all its modernity and size, retains the character of a partnership, adhering to a family's basic principles and ethical standards. Along the way various people in the organization have contributed guideline ideas, some reaching so far back in time that they are now thought of as traditions. Many Bechtel business philosophies have been translated into written policies and objectives, but others, equally honored and observed, have become ways of life that have never been formalized.

As Good As His Bond

During the firm's middle years there was a substantial amount of joint venture work. In this arrangement several contractors band together to share the risk on big projects, which usually are constructed wholly or largely by one of their number who is called the sponsor. W. A. Bechtel had been instrumental in developing this plan and he had some forceful opinions on the subject of joint venture partners.

He would team up only with contractors he considered competent and trustworthy. "If you can't trust a man's word you can't trust his signature," he used to say.

With men who had earned his confidence he would go a long way. It was not unusual for him to initiate ventures involving large sums with only a verbal understanding and a handshake. Written agreements, when there were any, were drawn up after the job was under way.

In later years, as operations grew more complex, such informality was incompatible with sound business practice. But this high degree of mutual respect and confidence became a valued heritage within these contractors' organizations and to this day is apparent in their business ethics and relations with one another.

Including some who have passed away, among the joint venture partners the Bechtels hold in especially high esteem are the Kaisers, Henry and Edgar; H. W. Morrison and Jack Bonny of Morrison-Knudsen; Felix Kahn of MacDonald & Kahn; Charles and Gilbert Shea of J. F. Shea; Bob Conyes of R. A. Conyes, Hal Price of H. C. Price; Walter and Lowell Dillingham of Hawaiian Dredging and Construction; Jack and Bob Pomeroy of J. F. Pomeroy; General L. J. Sverdrup of Sverdrup and Parcel, and Sir Godfrey Way Mitchell of George Wimpey, of London. In addition there are or have been fine joint venture relationships with such outstanding firms as Utah Construction & Mining, Raymond International, Brown & Root, Western-Knapp Engineering, Mannix, and H. G. Acres, as well as several European organizations.

Good Housekeeping

W. A. Bechtel believed that "cleanliness is next to godliness," a phrase he often used. From the early days of railroad construction he gave high priority to keeping jobs neat and orderly. Woe to the superintendent or section boss caught with disorganized piles of materials and debris! There was more to his interest than just appearance. An orderly job was likely to be an efficient job and in the long run, neatness promoted good working habits and straight thinking.

Further, he took pride in quality equipment which he kept in top condition, a policy that paid off in both time and money by helping to meet construction deadlines and earn the maximum return on his equipment investment.

From these beginnings good housekeeping and fully functioning equipment became traditional with the Bechtel organization. Today the basic principles of cleanliness and orderliness are applied to work procedures and working environments — in office and field. And keeping equipment in optimum condition includes everything from a caliper gauge to the company's big, highly advanced computer.

Industrial Relations Principles

In the heavy construction industry Bechtel is generally looked upon as being fortunate in its community, personnel and labor relations. The company has consistently enjoyed the confidence and loyalty of its employees and in the field has lost much less time in labor disputes than the industry average. The roots of these matters go deep, back to the first generation, before the days of public relations departments, labor negotiators and strong unions.

W. A. Bechtel was first of all a good citizen, wherever his work took him. He was considerate of neighbors in the countryside near his projects and respected his employees at office and job site. He was firm but fair, expecting a full day's work for a full day's pay. Because jobs were seldom near urban conveniences he set up construction camps, like other contractors of the time. His food was tasty and there was plenty of it. W. A. had the reputation of being a good feeder and before long he had his pick of workers. The good effects of these policies were not lessened as the organization grew larger.

Community and employee relations, and labor negotiations are still conducted on these principles. On the labor side, the building trades unions are recognized as the major source of competent, responsible construction people, and the company shows consideration for labor's problems as well as its own.

In developing countries, under circumstances resembling the railroad camp days, the same principles govern its dealings with nationals. Respect is shown for the dignity of the individual and his customs, he is treated fairly, compensated honestly, provided with clean camps and safe working conditions and often trained on site in various crafts.

Under John O'Connell's sponsorship of manpower services, the emphasis in the United States and Canada has been placed on standardizing labor contracts. The national labor agreement pioneered in the mid-1940's was one of the first in industrial construction. In recent years this activity has been carried forward on an industry-wide basis by the National Constructors Association, which O'Connell served as president. He was also chairman of the NCA group which, in conjunction with a high-level union committee, conducted a three-year study and jointly defined fair labor practices in the construction industry,

35

commonly referred to as the "Ten Commandments."

Through 25 years or more, Bechtel's keen interest in maintaining good community, employee and labor relations has been more evident in deeds than in words, and results have been excellent for all concerned.

Employee Benefits — A Worldwide Program

Salary rates uphold the company's principles of fair compensation. In fringe benefits Bechtel is a leader in its industry. Employees are offered comprehensive high-limit medical, surgical, hospital, accident and life insurance protection, with liberal company support.

In the United States and for Americans employed elsewhere there are two voluntary financial programs — the Bechtel Trust to which only the company and not the employee contributes, and the Bechtel Thrift Plan. In the Thrift Plan employees may invest up to a stated percentage of their compensation, which is matched by a company contribution in an amount determined annually. In 1966, '67 and '68 this was 75 cents for each dollar invested by the employee. For Canadian employees there is a combination of these plans with essentially the same benefits. In the United Kingdom and Australia there are pension schemes, and elsewhere, programs geared to conditions in the respective countries. In all cases the plans have been designed to encourage lifetime careers, providing maximum benefits to those with longest service.

Undivided Responsibility and Authority

From time to time observing businessmen have taken note of Bechtel's ability to attract the big complex jobs on a total performance basis. Such contracts, called "turn-key" in the trade, specify that a project will be delivered to its owner complete, ready to turn the key and start operating. Steve Bechtel has another term for this. He calls it undivided responsibility, which is more meaningful because it not only implies a start-to-finish service but defines the relationship between client and engineer-constructor for the duration of the project.

Steve summarized the company's philosophy several years ago when he said: "The client benefits because this arrangement makes possible the close coordination of engineering, procurement and construction with the continuity needed to deliver the most plant in the least time. The

36

validity of this point of view, which is traditional with us, has been borne out by results."

To questions about Bechtel's affinity for the turn-key contract, he replies: "We like responsibility. We have organized and prepared for it and we have scored our greatest successes when we have had control of projects in their entirety."

A Self-Contained Organization

This organizing and preparation took place in response to Steve's determination, even before he became Bechtel's president, to free the firm from the limitations of competitive bidding and contracts based on price alone, which was the case with its public projects in the 1930's. He sought a client relationship strengthened by confidence and understanding, with the greatest mutuality of objectives and maximum utilization of the resources of both the client's and Bechtel's organizations. He envisioned a service more comprehensive than construction, fixing his sights on developing a wholly self-contained economic technical organization able to handle projects of any size anywhere, from feasibility study to finished plant.

Steve knew that success would depend on providing advantages important enough to offset bidding, in which first price seldom indicates final cost. He concentrated on faster project completions with lower interest charges and earlier operating revenues, as well as the virtual elimination of duplication and waste, designed-in economies and a higher-quality project over-all.

Here was a big order. It called for something that then did not really exist: an inclusive professional organization staffed with specialists of many disciplines, knit together by strong planning and supervision, with excellent communications and coordination. Plainly, these requirements were not to be met in a hurry.

In the 1930's as Bechtel added more types of work and increased its engineering activities, the procurement services were expanded also. Then and later, both in the war-support and subsequent overseas operations, the organization continued to add experience in a range of additional business functions, all of which were to prove highly useful in developing a truly complete service.

37

The Complete Service in Action: Trans Mountain Pipeline

A very good example of what the company could do on an undivided responsibility project was the $93-million Trans Mountain Pipeline, built to carry crude oil over the Canadian Rockies from Alberta to the Pacific Northwest. Assured by studies that a strong market existed and encouraged by some interested oil companies, Bechtel dispatched a reconnaissance team to locate a route and report on feasibility before even an owner company had been put together for the pipeline.

When formed in 1951, S. D. Bechtel was elected Trans Mountain's first board chairman and R. L. Bridges, president; additionally, the Bechtel group assisted in arrangements for long-term financing and took a partial ownership position. Then Canadian Bechtel performed design, handled procurement and managed construction. Actual laying of the pipeline was done by independent Canadian firms.

Trans Mountain is a high-rise pipeline. It climbs the Rockies through unbelievably spectacular country to an elevation of 3800 feet. In its 715-mile length are formidable natural barriers — precipitous rock-walled canyons, rushing streams, slide-prone cliffs. All were mastered in a two-season push. The first delivery of Alberta crude was made in Vancouver in the fall of 1953. A spur into Washington State was built in 1954. The initial system of 24-inch pipe provided for 150,000 barrels per day. Since completion it has had several capacity increases, largely accomplished by Bechtel engineering and management.

Trans Mountain was important in Bechtel's development not only on its own merits but because it was the first major engineering-management job in which Bechtel was responsible for all design, engineering, procurement and management of construction as owner's representative.

Engineering-Management — A New Service

In a sense, engineering-management was an outgrowth of the complete turn-key concept. It requires the same type of diversified, functionally integrated organization, geared to handle all aspects of a project. The primary difference is that usually construction and other designated services are managed by Bechtel as the owner's agent and not for its own account, as prime contractor.

The company pioneered this arrangement, under which it assists in

Pipeline over the Canadian Rockies— construction of the Trans Mountain system in Red Pass, British Columbia.

Steep descent into Coquihalla Canyon, Trans Mountain Oil Pipeline.

establishing basic concepts; does planning, design and engineering; prepares budgets, specifications and schedules; procures materials and equipment; and coordinates and supervises the project's execution by selected contractors. Included are the awarding of contracts, inspection of work, delivery of the completed project and often, assistance with, or full responsibility for start-up. In critical cases, construction may be performed by Bechtel, in addition to engineering-management.

Volume under this arrangement has grown steadily. It is the form of contract most frequently used for foreign jobs on which contractors of the country are employed. For domestic projects such as large pipelines, where the nature of the work encourages simultaneous attack by a number of contractors under centralized direction, fast schedules can be accommodated readily. It lends itself well to certain other types of development such as water resources and hydroelectric programs of public districts, where Bechtel, as designer and consultant, is qualified to manage the construction. The owner retains control and approves major decisions but is freed from the necessity of assembling and phasing out a specialized project staff.

Negotiated (vs. Bid) Contracts

Comprehensive services calling for undivided responsibility are more suited to negotiation than bidding. Partly for this reason and partly because it serves the same major industrial firms again and again, Bechtel's negotiated work (including negotiated lump sum and other risk contracts) was, by the 1960's running between two-thirds and three-fourths of its total volume. Most of the company's progress away from dependence on bidding was made during the preceding decade, a trend that is continuing strongly.

"Many full-responsibility contracts are negotiated with our clients," Steve Bechtel says. "In practice this means that our position must be just as competitive as when a job is bid. We are firmly committed to the principles of free competition; our company has grown and thrived in fields which are highly competitive.

"Because our clients are well informed technically and experienced in the costs of their facilities, it is unlikely that the contracts they negotiate with competent engineer-constructors ever represent major differences in final costs from those obtainable by competitive bids. Often the costs of negotiated projects are lower."

Private and Public Clients

From the outset of Steve's presidency, service to industry, in contrast to government, has been an important Bechtel objective. A major trend line drawn for the past 30-year period would show that this goal has been met, but not without reversing direction a few times. In the early days the company's work was mostly for privately owned clients, the railroads. The depression years were marked by a swing the other way, to big public contracts — Hoover Dam, the Bay Bridge. Then, as private work in pipelines and oil refineries began to grow, the war came along and defense projects swung the balance back to the public side. But peace brought an almost instant change-over, and in the words chosen for its theme line, the Bechtel organization truly became "Engineers and Builders for Industry."

In the two decades since the war ended, the company's revenues from public work have seldom exceeded 12 per cent of the total in any year. In the 1960's, however, growth of Bechtel's involvement in public developments has generally paralleled its expanding volume in the private sector. Most of this business consists of projects for regional or district agencies, in such fields as water conservation and use, hydroelectric power, urban rapid transit, air and water pollution, salt water conversion, land use and environmental planning. In addition there have been numerous assignments from the Federal Government, principally in the space, missiles and nuclear programs.

The company has always made its services readily available to the Government whenever needed, especially for the national defense and activities requiring special technologies. But working for industry is its main forte.

Adding to the Mix — Diversification

In seeking to strengthen the organization it was inevitable that Steve Bechtel should arrive at another popular management technique — diversification. This he did many years ago with the first pipeline job. Again there was precedent, for in the early part of the century his father had branched out from railroad work into highway construction, and then into the building of water systems. Under the second generation the project list grew to include (after pipelines, in essentially chronological order) petroleum refineries, chemical plants, open pit mines and metallurgical plants, power generating stations, industrial plants, marine oil terminals, waterfront developments and oil field support facilities. All of these were on the company's experience roster by 1950.

From 1940 on there has been another kind of diversification — variety in job site geography. Overseas locations were limited at first, but from the start the foreign operation has had a stabilizing effect similar to that brought about by expanding the types of work.

Diversification has yielded Bechtel the anticipated benefit of balancing the workload but it has had other advantages as well. Much of the knowledge and many of the techniques required for the various types of projects are similar. To a considerable extent, personnel can be interchanged between divisions and groups as workloads rise and fall. A technical business finds this to be highly advantageous, for the quality of its manpower is paramount and diversification allows Bechtel to hold organization and build for permanence.

New fields are chosen with, as Steve Jr. has said, "the emphasis on selectivity.

"Before undertaking responsibilities of any type we carefully review the implications with respect to long-range Bechtel goals, growth potential, our competence and our available capacity at the time for this particular type of work. Consequently, whenever a new activity is initiated our organization is as fully prepared as good planning can make it."

Flexibility — An Important Bechtel Quality

Flexibility has been a familiar word in the Bechtel vocabulary for more years than anyone can remember. At first, flexibility simply meant that a man was able to adapt to changes in his responsibilities and environment. But as time went on the word took on broader meaning.

It is true that flexibility in this original sense is still very important. Such truly major projects of the 1950's as the Aden Petroleum Refinery or the smooth change-over in the 1960's from four to eight operating divisions could never have been brought off successfully without flexible people. Bechtel's people have developed a special knack for adapting.

Most of the key men have worked together for the better part of their business lives so they know each other intimately and can choose the right peg for any new hole in a hurry. The man selected may be adding to his present slate or moving into another field. In either case, schooled in a variety of assignments, he has learned to take hold of a new situation quickly, with the support and confidence of his associates.

Right Man, Right Place

Examples are numerous. These will illustrate:

Steve Jr. began in pipelining — first in the field, then in planning and later took on the direction of all pipeline work. Subsequently, he assumed broader executive duties which included the sponsorship of international activities and increasingly important corporate responsibilities as a director and officer of ascending rank.

Bill Waste moved from purchasing to general administration, then into shipbuilding; returned to manage administration and to sponsor both administrative and refinery-chemical activities.

Perry Yates, in his early years an engineer-builder of dams, headed the wartime aircraft modification center, then refinery-chemical work and later, as executive sponsor — the power, industrial, mining-metals, and scientific development activities.

John Kiely, shipbuilder, transferred at war's end to power and as the years passed, undertook the management and sponsorship of domestic activities in power, industrial, mining-metals, rapid transit, land use and urban planning.

Jerry Komes made the transition from shipbuilding to the management of industrial work, then to the overseas organization and on to direction and sponsorship of all international operations, as well as pipelines worldwide.

John O'Connell, shipyard labor coordinator, managed Bechtel's industrial relations, then further widened his field to include the senior direction of refinery and chemical activities.

In addition to changes in their functional duties, all of these men advanced from line operations to top executive responsibilities. They typify the adaptability of people in this flexible organization.

43

Flexibility Acquired Broader Meaning

Flexibility is essential to diversification; actually it is hard to separate cause and effect here, for the two go hand in hand. Today in management's view, flexibility also means the ability to look objectively at new types of work, to decide judiciously and provide competent organization when the decision is affirmative.

It likewise means flexibility in matching contract conditions and project procedures to client interests. Although zealous in guarding its professional integrity, Bechtel is surprisingly versatile in the service options it offers — preferably turn-key or engineering-management, but also engineering, construction or management separately or in any reasonable combination.

In size of job, as well, the company is flexible. It has the problem of keeping a big staff fully occupied. Relatively small, short-term jobs help to balance and maintain the workload. "Sometimes our clients will think a job too small for us," said an unnamed Bechtel executive quoted by Engineering News-Record.

"This really bugs us. We've started some of our best client relationships on small jobs."

Private Ownership by Active Management

Self-made men managing a professional service business of their own making might be expected to hold some positive opinions about its ownership. Those in Bechtel do. They believe their type of personalized, professional organization functions best under the private ownership of its active members.

"No widows or orphans," Steve likes to say. He means that men invited into the owner group — in all, some 50 plus or minus — agree that only those active in the business may own stock and that if any man should die or retire, his stock will be sold to the corporation or to the other stockholders.

An important advantage of having identical management and ownership is freedom of decision. Management can pursue objectives and serve clients according to the dictates of its own judgment. Action can be taken promptly in this line of business where delay may be hazardous.

Finally on this matter, the Bechtels think ownership should be proportional to the responsibilities borne by each participant. Parenthetically, participation in ownership ties in the risks and rewards, which involves senior management directly in profits and losses.

The private ownership philosophy has worked well. The company has not had a loss year in more than two decades.

Compensating the Producers

Good performance, the Bechtels believe, should reward the performers — which leads to another traditional philosophy.

Steve has always had an agreeable urge to remunerate outstanding people generously. It is a policy Steve Jr. continues. Profit sharing for the key producers and benefit programs like the Trust and Thrift Plans for long-term employees are well established company practices.

People who show real potential are moved up as rapidly as they are ready for heavier responsibilities. The upper level is the real goal. Once there they find themselves in a very agreeable financial climate; not, it should be quickly added, in balmy weather inducing relaxation, but rather, in an invigorating atmosphere that stimulates keen thinking, long hours and hard work.

Rewarding the upper bracket also generates a healthy response lower down. Or so it has proved with Bechtel. The incentive is strong, opportunities for advancement are numerous and employees know that as openings occur they will receive first consideration.

Future Leaders

Because of the cyclic nature of the business very few heavy construction firms have achieved to a comparable degree the planned continuity in management attained by many major industrial companies. Even before taking Bechtel out of the contractor category, Steve was laying the groundwork to develop an on-coming sequence of leaders in successive age groups. This process was later intensified and refined by Steve Jr., who has applied, as appropriate, many techniques of the present-day management sciences.

Continuity

In this company, continuity begins at the top with a chief executive

45

who is the third member of his family to hold that responsibility. His chief support is by men who, as stated, mainly came up through the ranks and thus provide the continuity of long association together. In addition, Bechtel is notable among engineer-constructors for having so many employees with 10 to 20 or more years of service. Consistent growth has been an important factor, providing continuous opportunities for advancement.

Good results are being obtained from internal training programs, including management development courses conducted by the University of California. The latter, the first of their kind, caused Business Week to report in 1965: "Bechtel has taken accredited university teaching, tailored it to its specific needs, and exported it to the company's principal offices around the world. The program may prove to be a substantial move toward executive self-sufficiency."

Pride in Accomplishment

Bechtel executives sometimes remind each other that money isn't everything. "Money was important to us but it was never the most important goal," the senior Steve says, and those who have known him over the years will agree.

Some rewards cannot be banked. Back at the start W. A. Bechtel learned to relish the stimulation, joy in activity and pride of accomplishment that gratify the builder. These considerations had a strong influence on his decision to cast his lot with construction. Down through the intervening years his descendants and their associates have shared these satisfactions.

But if there were not substantial funds little could be done. In this type of business a sound financial statement is a reliable indication of competence. The balance sheet should show an adequate net worth and the only part of the money flow that can be retained is profit.

Profit Makes Growth Possible

On this important subject the company has formalized its objective as being "to earn a fair profit commensurate with the quality and extent of the services rendered and the risks taken. In so doing, to take into account the continuing development of our organization and its

46

Continuity: Three generations carry on the family tradition of keeping in touch with the field—Riley, Grandad Steve, Gary, father Steve Jr. on a 1960 inspection trip.

At the 1966 home office picnic these four veterans represented 140 years of service. From left: Perry Yates, Steve Bechtel, V. G. "Heinie" Hindmarsh, and Bill Waste. Annual Bechtel family picnics are cherished traditions in many parts of the world; in recent years more than 5000 have attended the San Francisco event.

relationship with employees, clients, suppliers, subcontractors, the construction and other industries, government and the general public."

That brief statement condenses into 50 words the profit philosophy of three Bechtel generations.

"Profit makes accomplishment possible," says Perry Yates. "Profit earned by our client companies enables them to add to plant with new construction projects. A fair return for our work permits us to finance growth and improvement. Clients get the advantage of having organized technical experience and know-how available whenever they need it, tied together in a corporate structure of substance.

"We make our living in sophisticated fields where good work is mandatory and price is effectively controlled by the competitive system. Within these limitations there is room for an outstanding organization that provides its clients with important values not otherwise available. This is the place Bechtel aims to occupy, and in all fields where we have succeeded in so establishing ourselves we enjoy profitable operations."

CHAPTER FOUR

The First Half Decade: 1951-1955

The year 1951 was not very old before it became apparent that Steve Bechtel's optimistic message of the previous year-end had been on the conservative side. On-going work was substantial, more flowed in and the backlog rose higher and higher.

By the time 1951 had closed 30 new projects were in the fold, all awarded since the start of the preceding year. This work included more than 1200 miles of pipelines, three refinery jobs, four chemical plants, four steam power stations and ten industrial plants. The largest were the 600,000-kilowatt Pittsburg steam-electric station in California, an oil field development and support program in Sumatra and the Orinoco mining project in Venezuela.

Pittsburg was a milestone of sorts; it was the biggest generating plant yet for Bechtel and the largest in the State. The work in Sumatra involved gathering lines and centers in an oil field near Pakanbaru, a central pumping station, a 17-mile pipeline to a terminal on the Siak River and a deepwater shipping terminal at its mouth, 93 miles to the east. This was the start of a development which would be augmented five years later in still more comprehensive construction programs.

Mountain of Iron

The Orinoco iron ore project was the most important of the time in its industry. The client, a subsidiary of United States Steel Corporation, retained Bechtel to coordinate construction and administration. Most of the construction was performed by others. This project marked the company's return to mining and related activities, a field that before long would again assume major proportions among its specialties.

The three-year Orinoco development opened a vast new source of high-grade iron ore, helping to offset the approaching exhaustion of rich domestic deposits. It was one of U. S. Steel's first and biggest over-

49

seas investments and is, without doubt, the largest iron ore producing facility in South America. Cerro Bolivar, the mine site, is a 1500-foot hill one mile wide by four miles long. It was estimated to contain a half billion tons of ore, averaging 63.5 per cent iron by dry analysis, enough to assure a long, useful life of major production. By 1966 the output had risen to nearly 15 million long tons per year, several times the production originally scheduled.

For all of its riches, the site was in a primitive region in the interior of Venezuela, reached only by trails. Consequently, it was necessary to provide everything needed for a transportation system as well as the mining facilities. The principal units were the mine, a new port and townsite built at the junction of the Orinoco and Caroni Rivers, another townsite adjacent to the ore body at Cerro Bolivar, 90 miles of main line railroad and a 90-mile highway connecting the mine area with the new port, ore handling facilities and various appurtenant features required for a project of this type and magnitude.

Senior Management Team Strengthened

Bechtel's growing workload and larger organization called for further strengthening of the executive structure late in 1951. In January of 1952 S. D. Bechtel announced the new lineup. Bechtel Corporation now had 15 directors and 11 vice presidents in addition to three who were board members. Steve Jr. became a director at this time. The duties of six senior officers were increased. W. E. Waste was elected to the executive vice presidency and J. P. Yates, G. S. Colley Jr., J. K. Doolan, V. G. Hindmarsh and V. W. Rosendahl were named senior vice presidents. The newly elected vice presidents included J. R. Kiely, J. W. Komes, C. T. Draney, A. J. Orselli, J. S. Sides and W. R. Ayers.

In acquainting the organization with the realignment, Steve added:

"A fact readily apparent to all employees is that every executive is a seasoned Bechtel veteran. I am highly gratified that this is so, for the ability to move men up through the ranks is a credit both to the men and the organization."

Within the next two years several further changes took place. In 1952 and 1953, J. F. O'Connell, J. N. Landis and F. W. Meyer were

Orinoco Project: Loading ore for a 90-mile rail trip and transshipment to the United States.

George Colley (center) points out benching activity at the Cerro Bolivar mine to Kenneth and Steve Bechtel during a 1953 visit.

Puerto Ordaz, new marine ore terminal and community built at the junction of the Orinoco and Caroni Rivers.

Visiting the Contra Costa power plant on dedication day, August 29, 1951, were W. E. Waste, J. R. Kiely, S. D. Bechtel, V. W. Rosendahl, E. J. Garbarini, S. D. Bechtel Jr. and K. K. Bechtel.

The largest new power station west of the Mississippi made headlines—James B. Black, then president of Pacific Gas and Electric, and S. D. Bechtel at Pittsburg, California, in 1954.

elected vice presidents. S. D. Bechtel Jr., who had been appointed vice president in charge of U. S. and Canadian pipeline operations in 1952, was elected treasurer of the Corporation in 1953, upon the retirement of the late George Walling.

George Walling had joined the company ten years earlier to act as a financial and tax executive, after long service with an international firm of accountants. He had been the treasurer of Bechtel Corporation since its formation, and a director. His role in the company's development in the mid-century years was substantial; he had been instrumental in establishing the structural patterns of virtually all the Bechtel companies of that period.

A Great Builder

At the end of 1953 Van Rosendahl left to look after his personal interests, terminating 15 very active years. As officer, director and a ranking executive of the associated Bechtel companies, he managed the big Canol war emergency pipline project and went on to give senior direction to overseas activities and pipeline operations everywhere. Many of the largest and most difficult jobs had been his executive responsibilities — the Trans-Arabian, I.P.C., Trans Mountain and Lakehead pipelines, as well as the large oil installations in the Middle East and Sumatra. Likewise, as a member of the top team Rosendahl's foresight and judgment were of inestimable value during those formative years.

CBL's President; a New Treasurer

Meanwhile the company's Canadian subsidiary was growing rapidly, pacing the expansion of Canada's young petroleum industry. Contributing to the organization's success was Sidney M. Blair, the highly regarded engineer and executive who had managed Bechtel's Toronto headquarters since 1949. Appropriate to his role, he was elected president of Canadian Bechtel Limited in December of 1953.

In another corporate staffing move, R. D. Grammater was named treasurer of Bechtel Corporation in November of 1954, succeeding S. D. Bechtel Jr., who had served in that capacity since George Walling's retirement. And in December Grammater was elected a vice president.

There was nothing spectacular about the expansion that brought about this increase in the senior management population. Growth was steady and essentially uniform throughout the operation. Although the scope of activities continually increased, Bechtel's basic involvement remained in energy and natural resources development.

Electric Energy

The volume of power work rose rapidly in the first half of the 1950's. Within a short time the company took a leading position among engineer-constructors of steam-electric generating facilities. Its power projects were then located in the western states, where the electric utilities were adding to generating capacity at an even faster rate than the country as a whole. Following soon after the Contra Costa and Pittsburg stations came new plants near Phoenix, Arizona; at El Segundo and Long Beach in the Los Angeles area; at Eureka and Morro Bay on the California coast; and at Salt Lake City and Price, Utah.

Then, in 1953, Bechtel was asked to complete a big new power plant in Joppa, Illinois, which had been engineered and about one-third built by another company. Construction had come to a virtual halt on this 940,000-kilowatt giant following prolonged and bitter labor disputes.

When Bechtel took over, it shut down the job immediately. John O'Connell met with international and local union officers, hammered out new project contracts, and set up the machinery for airing grievances. Opposing union factions countered with threats, fights and lawsuits. But the responsible international labor leaders and Bechtel stood firm and won in the courts. When work began under Al Orselli it went ahead under relatively peaceful conditions. The company put its four of the six generating units on the line one after the other, completing the plant in the fall of 1955.

Joppa was a pointed example of the importance of labor relations. Time after time the depth and strength of the organization was put to the test and it took the best efforts of Perry Yates, O'Connell, Orselli, and dozens of others to get the job done. Joppa served to introduce Bechtel favorably to the electric utilities east of the Mississippi under very difficult circumstances; from that time on the western engineer-constructor's domestic power projects were nationwide in geography.

The Board in 1954: standing, from left, W. R. Ayers, corporate secretary; directors J. M. Rogers, J. L. Simpson, K. K. Bechtel, J. K. Doolan, R. L. Bridges, J. P. Yates, S. D. Bechtel Jr.; seated, G. S. Colley Jr., S. D. Bechtel, W. E. Waste.

S. M. Blair at the time of his election to Canadian Bechtel's presidency in 1953.

I. R. Caraco was assistant manager of engineering at Vernon when the El Segundo power plant was built in the mid-1950's.

Reviewing plans at Ferndale, Washington, in 1953 for the Pacific Northwest's first major oil refinery were B. B. Jennings, president of Socony-Vacuum; R. L. Minckler, president of General Petroleum; and S. D. Bechtel.

Keeping ahead of the work may require traveling 50,000 miles or more a year on trips like this—Bob Bridges and Steve Bechtel Jr. en route to a South American project.

On tour of three Korean power plants under construction in mid-1950's—Jerry Komes, over from the home office and Cliff Pehl, resident manager of the projects.

Nuclear Power Group

The first successful use of nuclear energy for the production of electric power — accomplished by the U. S. Atomic Energy Commission in the Bechtel-built experimental reactor facility EBR-1 in Idaho — took place on December 21, 1951. But somewhat earlier the company, the power utilities, and major manufacturers of electrical equipment had become keenly interested in the future of nuclear power.

During 1951 Bechtel and Pacific Gas and Electric had formed a study team at the AEC's invitation, one of four original atomic industrial groups. After two years the two western companies joined with six eastern and midwestern utilities to set up a larger study organization known as Nuclear Power Group. Based in Chicago, this body was asked by the AEC to prepare economic and design studies covering the application of promising type nuclear reactors to commercial electric power plants. A review of existing experimental reactors and proposed designs led to the conclusion that the dual-cycle boiling water reactor held the greatest promise at that time for immediate application.

Early Nuclear Power Activities

As yet no commercial nuclear power plant had been authorized by the AEC and in the entire United States construction began on only one during the first half of the 1950's. Bechtel, however, kept closely in touch with Government and industry developments. Following EBR-1 at the Idaho test station, the company constructed an adjacent chemical processing plant in which spent fuel elements from the reactors were reprocessed to salvage uranium and usable fission products. In view of the great future predicted for industry in reprocessing nuclear fuel, this and a later plant by Bechtel in New York — the first under private ownership — were important pioneer developments. The Idaho facility also researched techniques of handling and welding the special alloy metals required for nuclear equipment. These activities contributed valuable experience to the mounting body of knowledge which eventually led to the economic feasibility of nuclear power.

Likewise, the Bechtel organization was adding to its own competence in the new field. It provided services on a materials testing accelerator project, conducted an engineering study for cooling a materials production reactor, and designed and supervised construction and observation of electric distribution facilities in AEC demonstration tests in Nevada. Nevertheless, major involvement would wait until the second half of the decade, when the first big nuclear power project took shape.

Refineries — a Brisk Market

In the ten years immediately following the war the world requirement for petroleum products more than doubled. A great change also took place in the demand by type of product, particularly in the 1950's. The domestic market for high-quality motor fuels rose greatly in response to the ascendancy of high-powered, high-compression automobile engines. This led to what the industry called the octane race, prompting a great increase in refinery construction. Additionally, expanding U. S. sales encouraged the refiners to locate new plants in virgin territories.

This was so in the Pacific Northwest where the continuous availability of crude oil through the Trans Mountain pipeline resulted in the construction of petroleum refineries where none had existed before. Overseas there was a big increase in fuel oil demand, bringing into existence large new plants like the Aden Refinery and expansions elsewhere, as in Saudi Arabia and Kuwait.

Washington's Three Grass-Roots Plants

Two of the Northwest refineries were projects of the early 1950's, a 35,000-barrel plant at Ferndale and a 50,000-barrel complex near Anacortes, both in the State of Washington. The third, of 40,000 barrels daily capacity, also near Anacortes, was a later (1957-'58) job, but so properly a part of the over-all pipeline-plus-market pattern that it merits attention here. All were turn-key, undivided responsibility projects — design, procurement and construction — amounting, in the aggregate, to $175 millions. And all were "grass-roots" jobs, meaning that these plants were entirely new, from the grass up.

Together with another refinery across the national border in British Columbia, these three plants and the Trans Mountain pipeline paid Bechtel handsomely for the initiative of its president in launching the pipeline venture.

It must be admitted, however, that at least one of these important

Puget Sound Refinery, one of three grass-roots oil processing complexes designed and built in western Washington.

Among key men responsible for success of the Aden Refinery project were Heinie Hindmarsh, sponsoring director, and Jim Brady, his deputy (third and fourth from left); Ro Ross (far left), assistant project manager; Fred Brown, project manager; Walt Sims and Jim Leaver, assistant project managers.

On arrival from the States, John L. Simpson was welcomed to the Aden Refinery job by Jim Leaver.

"by-product" jobs was anticipated. Indeed, the chief executive of the first Washington refinery client was the man who had originally kindled Steve's interest in building the pipeline over the Canadian Rockies. During a luncheon conversation in which he had pointed out the need and opportunity for the pipeline he had also mentioned his company's willingness to build a refinery at its western terminus!

Fast Work in Aden

Aden was a special case of another kind. The owner company, having lost its largest plant to Iranian nationalization, put a premium on speed. Bechtel got the contract — full responsibility and authority — with a daily bonus or penalty clause guaranteeing delivery two years ahead of competing British proposals and a year earlier than that of another American firm.

The schedule was tight, the difficulties enormous. The project consisted of a 120,000-barrel refinery — the biggest refinery up to that time built in one operation — its power plant and other appurtenances, a deepwater oil port, a tank farm and a permanent community. The contract was signed in November, 1952. A London firm became Bechtel's joint venture associate and undertook the harbor work.

Dependable veteran Heinie Hindmarsh deferred his retirement to head the Aden job as project sponsor. Based in London, he traveled the world on all aspects of the work, delegating important responsibilities to his younger colleagues. Many were "Heinie's boys," as they were known within the organization, developed over the years under his able guidance.

Gene Lippa, stateside, was responsible for the engineering, procurement and recruiting, with Glenn Buchanan as deputy. Jim Brady was project general manager; Roy McAuliffe had charge of United Kingdom operations; Porter Thompson was chief engineer; Rudy Grammater headed administration and Fred Brown supervised construction.

Biggest, Most Explosive Construction Camp

The project's remote location at the southwest tip of the Arabian peninsula and the near total lack of a local labor force required recruiting workers in many countries and transporting them to Aden, and housing, feeding and servicing at job site more than 14,000 altogether. They were of 15 nationalities, including Americans, Britons, Italians, Dutch, Indians, Levantines, Adenese, Arabs and Somalis. Brought into close proximity and exposed to one another for some two years, their differences of race, nationality and religion posed the constant threat of conflict. They were divided, prudently, into distinct, self-contained camps. Eleven mess halls catered to various tastes. It is a credit to Bechtel that no serious trouble developed. On the contrary, worker morale was excellent for the life of the job.

Supply was another outsized problem. Nearly 2000 ship arrivals were logged during construction, bringing in a third of a million tons of freight. An additional 600 tons of high priority items came by air. Materials and equipment were procured worldwide in 22 countries, with due regard for delivery, quality and price. If the Trans-Arabian and IPC pipelines had involved major supply and transportation activities, Aden proved to be the ultimate in logistic exercises.

"By terms of the contract the refinery was to be ready to start operating on December 1, 1954," the London Times reported on August 8th of that year, and added: "but the main distillation unit came into operation on July 29th." One after another the rest of the processing plants went on stream until, on October 15, 1954, the big project was officially declared complete.

It was a great performance by an outstanding project team, earning the joint venture a substantial bonus, both for delivery months ahead of schedule and a reduction below estimate in the final cost. Characteristically, those primarily responsible for the job's success shared generously in the profit.

More Types of Work, More Countries

The company's overseas work, which had been largely in Middle East oil developments, now began to diversify into mining and power, and to spread geographically. The Orinoco mining project had materialized at the same time as the Aden Refinery, marking the organization's return to Venezuela, the country where its foreign operations had started some 12 years earlier. Then in 1954, the Republic of Korea, with support from U. S. foreign aid funds, retained Bechtel to design and construct

Aden Petroleum Refinery: power house, process facilities and housing.

three steam-electric power plants. Built in a two-and-a-half-year program and finished ahead of schedule and under budget, these plants virtually doubled Korea's existing electric generating capacity.

Meanwhile Canada, always dependent on other countries for petroleum, had located large reserves of oil and natural gas in Alberta. Thereafter, in the short six-year span from 1946 to 1952, that country's crude production multiplied 11 times, setting in motion oil pipeline and refinery construction programs on both sides of the border. Large-scale development of the natural gas resources did not begin at once, awaiting decisions by the Federal and Provincial Governments.

A comprehensive review of these six years in the Canadian oil industry was published in 1953 by the Petroleum Press Service of London. The review included a roll call of the most important projects of the period. There were three major oil pipelines, refineries in Canada and Washington State, and a petroleum products packaging plant. Of the 13 jobs listed, 8 were Bechtel responsibilities.

One of the most interesting facets of this work was the successful laying of the world's deepest underwater pipeline. In a spectacular crossing under the Straits of Mackinac between Lake Huron and Lake Michigan, two 20-inch crude oil pipelines were pulled across a four-mile channel. The steel pipe, nearly an inch thick, was laid to a depth of 238 feet. The feat was accomplished on the the 650-mile Lakehead Extension of the Interprovincial system, linking that Canadian crude oil pipeline with its market in the Sarnia refining district of Ontario via a short cut through the United States. Bechtel provided engineering-management for the Lakehead Extension and built part of the project.

Engineering, United Nations Style

Canada, England, Italy, the Philippines, the Middle East, South America, Korea. Active in 10 countries by January 1, 1955, Bechtel's geography was expanding rapidly. If not yet fully international the organization was rapidly becoming so, especially in personnel. A count made in 1955 at the home office turned up 117 employees educated in foreign universities; they had credentials from 77 institutions. Canadian universities led, but the rest of the world was well represented — colleges in the United Kingdom, in virtually all countries of Western Europe and

Scandinavia; Latin America, the Philippines, Lebanon and Turkey; even some in iron curtain lands — Poland, Hungary, Russia and China. It could be said fairly that people on staff had acquired their technical knowledge in many parts of the world.

In little more than a decade even these figures were to grow several times over. By 1967 the depth of the company's international mix among graduate engineers and technical people worldwide was shown by the fact that among them were men and women with 888 degrees from universities outside the United States, representing nearly 20 per cent of all college degrees in the company's ranks.

1955: Topside Advancements

Bechtel has always been a dynamic organization from top to bottom. Responding to sustained growth and the consequent need for more management capacity, several important additions were now made to the upper group.

Foremost of these was the election of a new senior vice president. Steve Jr., who had proved himself ready for a heavier load, was named to that post in 1955. Somewhat earlier he had taken charge of all pipeline and engineering activities in the United States and Canada, and he continued to hold these responsibilities in his new position.

John Kiely was elected to the Board of Directors where the vigor and judgment evident in his handling of the Power Division could be given still broader application.

New Talent

In 1955, also, the company welcomed four newcomers from the outside. In March, Edward J. Mahoney Jr. joined the Pipeline Division as a vice president and special assistant to Steve Jr., to aid in the development of new business. He had successfully operated his own pipeline construction firm, which had been one of the best of the Lakehead Extension contractors working under Bechtel's supervision. Rapid expansion of the pipeline industry had convinced him that affiliation with Bechtel offered greater opportunity for future growth than independent activity. In 1959 he became Pipeline Division manager, and four years later was named to head corporate business development.

Also in March of 1955, Perry Yates announced the appointment of John P. Buehler as an executive engineer in the Power Division. Buehler had just retired from the United States Corps of Engineers after 20 years of service. He had been responsible for overseeing public works on the Columbia River, and had been chairman of the American Section of the International Columbia River Engineering Committee concerned with water matters of mutual interest to the United States and Canada. In 1958 he was appointed manager of business development, engineering and design for the Hydro Department and in 1962 was elected to a vice presidency as manager of that department. When the Hydro and Transportation Division was formed in 1966, Buehler was named division manager.

Mynderse Van Hoesen joined in May, 1955, as vice president and legal counsel. As a partner in the law firm that served the company, he had been occupied almost entirely with Bechtel work for the preceding 15 years. Van Hoesen thus brought to his new position a close acquaintance with the company's past activities. Under his direction the Legal and Insurance Department expanded in size and usefulness. He retired from operational duties in 1964 but continues to handle important special assignments.

The business development section of the Refinery Division, then under Vice President Charles T. Draney, announced the arrival of Dr. Martin de Simo in June of 1955. A Fellow of the American Institute of Chemical Engineers and of the American Institute of Chemists, he is a recognized authority on petrochemical processing. In 1962 he was elected a vice president of Bechtel Corporation. As its eastern representative and in the home office, de Simo's knowledge of petrochemical technology and economics and his wide acquaintance with the industry's leaders served the company well. On his retirement in 1967 he was named a Bechtel consultant.

Where the Future Leaders Were

Many who were to emerge later as officers were giving evidence of their capabilities, as several examples will show. Ed Garbarini was sent to Southern California in 1955 as area manager, with headquarters in the Vernon office. Bill Ness headed a design group as project engineer

When Alberta's Premier E. C. Manning (right) reviewed Canadian Bechtel's work on the Trans-Canada Pipeline, Bechtel's E. J. Mahoney Jr. and C. S. Coates, president of Trans-Canada, were his guides.

J. P. Buehler (right), who came with Bechtel in 1955 and has subsequently headed hydro and transportation activities, is shown checking the site axis of Homestake Dam in Colorado with Charles Content, chief geologist.

Dr. Martin de Simo, shortly after joining the company's refinery and chemical staff, conferring with Charles T. Draney.

on a new power plant being constructed in Honolulu. Glenn Buchanan, recently back from Aden, moved down the California coast to a grass-roots refinery project near Santa Maria, California. And John Merryman, who had spent virtually all of his business life with Bechtel, was named project manager of the big Dresden nuclear power plant.

1950-'55: A Rising Curve

Five years after mid-century the Bechtels could measure progress in their company's level of effort by a good round number — it had doubled. Allowing for peaks and valleys caused by the interplay of varying settlement dates and the calendar year, the business had grown on average a full 20 per cent a year.

The backlog, which had leveled briefly, was turning up again. Non-manual, salaried employees (a more reliable yardstick for assessing trends than the fluctuating labor force in the field) had increased from 2000 to over 3000 worldwide. And this manpower had more breadth and depth of technical capability, greater strength and competence.

Much of the company's population growth was taking place in the engineering classifications. Strict emphasis on quality in hiring was paying off by raising the company's professional stature and involvements. Further, the 50 per cent staff buildup required improvements in organizational structure and better over-all coordination. These objectives Bechtel was meeting but even so, it was still in an early stage of evolution into today's much larger, more versatile organization.

The Four Operating Divisions

Operations were being handled by four divisions, named for their main classes of work: Refinery, Power, Industrial and Pipeline. Activities in Canada were the province of the wholly owned Canadian subsidiary as the contracting party but most of the work, as with other international projects at this time, was assigned to one or more of the four divisions. Jobs located off the North American continent were given close attention by a separate group concerned solely with overseas operations.

Planning Ahead for the Second Half

Like all postwar years, 1955 was a good one for the company. In his holiday message to the organization, Steve Bechtel noted that it had been a busy time, "marked by achievements in the United States and other parts of the Western Hemisphere and across the world in the Middle East and Korea. It has seen our entry into new countries . . . and the strengthening of old bonds . . .

"As we look ahead we contemplate the continuation of a very satisfactory volume in the petroleum, petrochemical and power industries — in which we have traditionally been effective. There are several fields that will receive stronger emphasis in future activities, including:

"*Pipelines* — We are on the threshold of pipeline programs which are without precedent in size and importance. The year 1956 will witness two great Canadian projects which will provide both western and eastern Canada with Alberta gas . . .

"*Nuclear Power* — This great source of energy is about to take its place with hydro and thermal power in most parts of the world. Our interests in the Nuclear Power Group and in the most outstanding nuclear power plant being built at this time are but a part of our activities in this tremendous field . . .

"*Water Resources* — In the west and elsewhere water resources are receiving the prime attention of some of our best engineering organizations. Standards of living, population movements and industrial expansion are all vitally geared to water resources and their proper development; accordingly we have been active and plan to be even more so in this significant field.

"The successful completion of a number of major projects on a turnkey basis, involving complete engineering, procurement and construction, proves the effectiveness of this type of contractual arrangement. We will emphasize this philosophy more strongly than ever.

"The entire program presents a splendid outlook. Our activities will be limited only by our capacity and our effectiveness — which, I can confidently say, are at the highest peak of any time in our history."

Rod and ball mills in an iron ore beneficiation plant, one of many such facilities completed by Bechtel.

CHAPTER FIVE

The Advancing Decade: 1956-1959

The organizational realignments that began in 1952 continued through the second half of the decade. From time to time these changes reflected normal attrition, as responsibilities passed from older to younger men. Jerome K. Doolan, a prominent example, resigned as a senior vice president and director at the end of 1955 and became a Bechtel consultant. Having completed his wartime assignment by closing out Calship, he had joined Bechtel's executive group in 1945 to develop and manage the Industrial Division. Under Jerry Doolan's able direction this unit became a major force in its field and established a strong foundation for the company's later industrial work.

Mostly, however, the changes of the 1950's were on the growth side, building organization in response to continuing expansion. In 1956 Jerry Komes was elected to the Board of Directors and in the following year Ed Garbarini was named a vice president.

The Executive Vice Presidents

The years 1957, '58 and '59 witnessed the most important organizational adjustments at senior level in the company's history up to that period. In 1957, Stephen D. Bechtel Jr. and Perry Yates were elected executive vice presidents, joining W. E. Waste in that position. During the preceding year Steve Jr. had been elected vice chairman of Canadian Bechtel Limited. John Kiely was appointed senior vice president of Bechtel Corporation and Sid Blair, Canadian Bechtel's president, was elected to the Board of the parent company.

Coordinating Committee

A new group was formed as an advisory body to coordinate operations and practices company-wide, working closely with the chief officer of each division. Called the Coordinating Committee, its first members were Bill Waste, chairman; Steve Jr., Perry Yates and George Colley. As stated, the committee was to be "active in divisional senior organizational affairs, to review proposed projects as to desirability and in relation to capacities and workloads, and to consider other key matters affecting the company's welfare for mutual information and advice."

The committee has continued its work; its membership has changed and increased, and to some extent its functions have been modified, but its importance in unifying Bechtel's expanding activities has never flagged. Its effectiveness has been amplified by permanent specialized committees concerned with engineering, construction, and business development, which report to the Coordinating Committee and provide cross-pollination of information and ideas, company-wide.

Overseas Division

In 1957, also, operations beyond the North American continent were centralized in a new Overseas Division under George Colley, senior vice president, with Jerry Komes, vice president, as deputy. Colley had been active in international work for many years, in fact, had been the advance scout and later, manager of Bechtel's first overseas project.

George S. Colley Jr.

George Colley's highly productive career as an engineer and builder came to a tragic end on July 14, 1958 in Baghdad, Iraq, when he was killed by a street mob during a civil uprising. Although only 56, he had been a central figure in Bechtel for over a quarter century. Able, resourceful and courageous, George Colley was also a man with great human qualities and no one outside his family felt his loss more keenly than his friends and colleagues in the organization to which he had devoted most of his business life.

Following George Colley's death, Jerry Komes took over the top operating duties in the Overseas Division and was elected a senior vice president of Bechtel Corporation and executive vice president of the foreign subsidiaries.

The Sponsor Concept

At that time Steve Jr. added to his Pipeline Division and Canadian Bechtel responsibilities the sponsorship of all international activities.

72

The sponsor concept has been part of the Bechtel scheme for a long time. It places prime responsibility for total conduct of a designated part of the business squarely on one or another of the ranking senior executives. Reporting to the sponsor is another executive who has the key operating authority for a specific activity. In this way all divisions, major staff functions and many of the bigger projects fit into a plan of organization where decisions of major importance emanate from the top.

Division Titles Amplified

During 1958 the titles of three operating divisions were changed to describe their expanded scope more accurately. The recently formed Overseas Division became the International Division in recognition of its increasingly global nature. The Refinery Division was renamed Refinery and Chemical Division, reflecting the growing importance of its business with the chemical industry. The Power and Industrial Division's work now included all power — steam-electric, hydroelectric and nuclear — as well as projects in the former Industrial Division's field, particularly in metals and other types of heavy industrial activity. Only the Pipeline Division's name remained unchanged.

Vice Presidents and a New Department

Three vice presidents were elected in 1958. The first, in April, was Harry F. Waste, who had recently returned to the home office and the Pipeline Division from Vancouver, where he had served as Canadian Bechtel's vice president and manager of pipeline engineering and management services.

In June, Perry Yates announced the formation of "a new department for development and applications research in many scientific fields." It began under W. Kenneth Davis, former director of reactor development, Atomic Energy Commission, who joined Bechtel as a vice president.

AEC research programs supervised by Davis included power reactors, nuclear propulsion for aircraft, missiles and naval vessels; as well as related work in metallurgy and chemical processing. Clearly, he was well qualified to establish Bechtel's new applied research group, which he managed until 1967 when he assumed business development duties, working closely with Charlie Draney in the international power and industrial operation.

Lou Killian, Bechtel's chief officer in the Middle East, moved to the home office in 1958 to begin new duties under Jerry Komes.

Fred Meyer and Al Orselli were active for many years in domestic refinery and chemical work before transferring to the international organization.

Harry Waste returned from service in Canada to major Pipeline Division responsibilities; Chuck Lester went to The Hague office as senior pipeline officer.

Robert A. Bowman was elected a vice president in December of 1958. He had joined the organization in 1951 after more than 20 years with a large American manufacturer of electric apparatus. After two years with Bechtel, he was named chief engineer, Power Division; later, division manager of engineering; and in 1966, manager, Power and Industrial Division. In 1965 Bowman received the American Society of Mechanical Engineers' George Westinghouse Gold Medal for "distinguished service in the power field."

Realignments; Further Additions to the Executive Team

The year 1959 opened with the president's announcement that senior operating responsibilities had been rearranged in two divisions. The changes involved John O'Connell and Al Orselli. O'Connell assumed responsibility for the Refinery and Chemical Division in addition to industrial relations. At the same time, Orselli was transferred to assist Jerry Komes in the expanding International Division.

In May, Clark Rankin was elected a vice president. He had then completed 25 years with Bechtel and was based in Europe with responsibility for pipeline construction there and in North Africa.

Later in the year Charlie Draney moved to the International Division from Refinery and Chemical to further strengthen the overseas operation and to take over direction of management services on a worldwide hotels construction program. Also at this time the New York office, with Porter E. Thompson as manager of technical services, was made the responsibility of Refinery and Chemical in an arrangement similar to the tie then existing between the Vernon office and the Power and Industrial Division.

Future Officers on the Move

Among others moving ahead, Gene Lippa in 1959 was well into his fifth year in London as resident manager and vice president of Bechtel International Limited. Glenn Buchanan, who had advanced to manager of refinery and chemical construction, was transferred to the International Division to manage stateside services.

Robert A. Cheatham, then project coordinator on a large aluminum

75

plant job in upper New York State, was appointed manager of industrial plant engineering. K. O. Taylor, veteran of the Hoover Dam project, having recently supervised several large hydro jobs and early field work on the Dresden nuclear power plant, was named divisional manager of construction for Power and Industrial. Also, I. R. Caraco had been advanced to manager of engineering at Vernon; W. H. Ness was appointed manager of steam plant engineering and John Merryman became manager of nuclear plant engineering in San Francisco.

Steadily and surely the future leadership was developing.

1959: Executive Committee Established, Given Broad Powers

In August the Board of Directors created the Executive Committee to perform many functions the Board itself had formerly carried out. The new committee consisted of six regular and two ex-officio members, and a secretary. Steve Jr. as its chairman became, in the absence of the president, the company's senior officer. Robert L. Bridges, John Kiely, Jerry Komes, Bill Waste and Perry Yates were the regular members and S. D. Bechtel and John L. Simpson the ex-officio members. Rudy Grammater was appointed secretary of the committee.

It was charged with determining policy in all matters not specifically reserved to the Board; in particular, with making decisions governing operations, business development and organizational and personnel affairs pertaining to the executive and managerial staff. Highly important, the Executive Committee was given authority to set financial policy, one of the functions performed from 1952 to 1959 by the Finance Committee which were absorbed at this time by the newly formed body.

Creation of the Executive Committee marked a major advance. As Steve Bechtel said in announcing its formation, "delegation of responsibility to this closely knit group will strengthen our organization and corporate structure. It also will free me to devote more attention to long-term planning and special policy matters."

A Major Voice

In addition, Steve Jr.'s Executive Committee chairmanship gave him increased authority. Years before formal recognition, his transition to top responsibility was smoothly under way. During the 1950's, father

The Executive Committee in the fall of 1966, from left: R. D. Grammater, R. L. Bridges, J. R. Kiely, J. P. Yates, S. D. Bechtel Jr., chairman, J. W. Komes, J. F. O'Connell; S. D. Bechtel and W. E. Waste, ex officio.

and son conferred frequently prior to making any decisions that would affect the future of the business.

"Steve will have to live with the results," the senior Bechtel reasoned, "so he should have a major voice."

They both knew the quickening pace was making heavier demands on the organization and would continue to do so. Further, Steve Jr. had prepared himself by education, observation and experience to cope with complex management problems. Already he was beginning to shape his future executive group into a strong cohesive team and to introduce improvements suggested by some of the newer developments in the management sciences.

Underlying Bechtel's growth in top personnel during the 1950's was its continuing success in building clientele. In this period of rising construction volume everywhere, the company steadily gained on the field by attracting the big, complex, imaginative projects. These, in turn, were constantly growing in number and size.

Refinery Business Was Up

Two trends were evident in refinery and chemical work. In the United States and Canada there was a substantial increase in chemical plant contracts. Overseas the refinery business was particularly brisk — between 1955 and 1960 Bechtel had three grass-roots refineries under way abroad in addition to two grass-roots jobs in the U. S. and two in Canada. Also, a big refinery expansion was in progress in the Middle East to uprate the Kuwait plant's throughput to 160,000 barrels daily.

Overcapacity Turned Things Around

These, together with numerous processing units being built in existing refineries, continued to preserve the prosperous pattern set early in the decade. But it was not to be "all roses" forever. In the second half of the 1950's oil processing capacity, especially in the United States, temporarily outran the demand, and the obvious result was a big reduction in refinery construction projects.

To meet the petroleum industry's earlier requirements nearly all engineer-constructors had enlarged their organizations. Consequently the drop in business, coming suddenly, hit many of them very hard. Bechtel executives were reminded that their company was still in a high-risk business. They truly appreciated the advantages of the diversification it had achieved. The company's lively activity in foreign refineries and domestic chemical plants took up part of the slack but even so, it became necessary to reduce staff for a time in the Refinery and Chemical Division and many were transferred to other divisions.

Alumina and Aluminum

Good things were happening in other types of work. In 1956 a large aluminum producer awarded Bechtel an expansion program that added more than 50 per cent to the capacity of a major alumina plant in Texas; later this client authorized the company to design and build an all-new aluminum reduction plant on the St. Lawrence River in upper New York. These contracts opened another very active industrial field for Bechtel.

Iron Ore Beneficiation Solved an Industry's Problem

In the light of subsequent developments, a third metals job initiated in 1957 was equally important. The Orinoco Project had furnished one answer to the diminishing supply of high grade U. S. iron ore; namely, the utilization of rich foreign deposits. Technology had produced another — the processing of low grade ores into iron concentrates at or near the mine for economical shipment. Called ore beneficiation, this solution to the problem has had a salutary effect on steelmaking economics and has come into wide use.

The previously mentioned 1957 job was an iron ore beneficiation plant using magnetic equipment to separate iron concentrate from crushed ore. Located at Moose Mountain, Ontario, it was Bechtel's introduction to this important specialty. With no let-up the company has been designing and building beneficiation plants ever since, as well as pelletizers, ore transportation and handling facilities, and has been stripping and benching ore bodies in many parts of the world.

Hydro's New Activity

The latter half of the 1950's brought a big upsurge in hydro business, both for water conservation and power generation. Historically, it was something of a renaissance, for this was a field the firm had entered 30 years earlier, in which activity peaked at Hoover Dam. Thereafter, there had been a general decline in this type of work and Bechtel's hydro volume dropped to an occasional job of modest size.

Now, following completion of several hydroelectric projects for California's major private utilities, the company was staffed and prepared for the bigger jobs to come.

Much of the new work was for public water and power districts. Bechtel's Hydro Department usually served as consultant, reporting on feasibility and preparing the basic plan on which bond elections and financing programs were based. Once under way, the company performed detail engineering and wrote specifications, supervised bidding and awards, and administered construction contracts, overseeing the work of selected contractors.

Centralization of these functions in one organization — especially one whose technical proficiency and reliability were respected by the major financial underwriters — had important advantages for the public districts. And from the company's standpoint, the engineering-contract administration arrangement was well suited to public work, as it met all legal requirements and placed Bechtel in an objective position to serve as the district's representative for the supervision of construction and other project services.

In three years nine new jobs were added to on-going hydro work. They ranged from a small powerhouse to a $200-million dam and hydroelectric development. Most of these contracts were in the larger categories and two involved programs of 10 or more years duration. Later this busy period would be seen in perspective as the revival of hydro activities which, by 1967, included over 9.3 million kilowatts of hydroelectric generating capacity, 47 dams, 26 powerhouses, 80 miles of water tunnels, and 42,000 feet of penstocks.

Special interest attached to two of the projects. On one, the Wells hydroelectric development on the Columbia River in Washington, an imaginative design saved the client nearly $15 millions, making the big project commercially feasible. Powerhouse and spillway were brought together in a single structure, conceived by Bechtel engineers and called a "hydrocombine." The powerhouse consists of 10 units, the spillway

Union Valley Dam on the Upper American River hydroelectric project in California.

of 11 bays with a power unit between each bay, providing a total capacity of well over 800,000 kilowatts. Fish handling facilities, hoists and switch-yard are all located on this one massive concrete block.

The other project, more accurately a "program," is the Upper American River Basin Development, a veritable stairway of power in the Sierra, serving the city of Sacramento, California. It is one of the most diverse hydroelectric schemes ever undertaken, involving almost every conceivable type of structure. Originally planned in four stages for construction over a 10-year period, the first three stages were completed in five years. Later, increased load requirements necessitated additions to a total of six stages, for completion in 11 years.

Dresden, Pioneer Commercial Nuclear Power Plant

In another power field — nuclear power — action was starting. Authorized in 1955, formal design began the following spring on the 210,000-kilowatt Dresden Nuclear Power Station. Bechtel had been retained as engineer-constructor by General Electric Company, the prime contractor. In part Dresden was an outgrowth of the Nuclear Power Group's studies and the NPG members contributed $15 millions to the project for research and development. G-E wrote a fixed price turn-key contract with the owner, Commonwealth Edison Company of Chicago, for $45 millions — far below the plant's real cost. At this figure the Illinois authorities could approve the project as reasonably near the expenditure required to build a conventional plant of comparable size. Thus, financed entirely through private initiative and cooperation, America's first truly large nuclear power station went into design.

Detail engineering followed and construction started early in 1957. By September, 1959, Bechtel's work was essentially complete. Dresden reached initial full-rated capacity in the following June and was dedicated on October 12. Representatives of Government, business and science heard the chairman of the U. S. Atomic Energy Commission term it "the largest, most efficient, most advanced" nuclear power plant in the world. The AEC chairman was, in point of interest, John A. McCone, former colleague and one-time president of Bechtel-McCone.

"Dresden did more to establish commercial nuclear power than any other single project," Steve Bechtel has said.

82

Dresden Nuclear Power Station, Illinois, was America's first major nuclear power plant.

R. J. Cordiner, General Electric board chairman, attached a plate to the control console during Dresden's dedication, assisted by John A. McCone, AEC chairman, and Willis Gale (right), board chairman of Commonwealth Edison. Participating (from left) Philip Sporn, president, American Electric Power; S. D. Bechtel and Norman Sutherland, president, Pacific Gas and Electric.

W. K. Davis and J. N. Landis represented the engineer-constructor when construction began on the Big Rock Point Nuclear Power Station.

"It set precedent for the utilization of an independent engineer-constructor and established the roles of the owner, engineer-constructor and manufacturer in this type of work. It justified public utility boards in authorizing additional nuclear power plants by pioneering a financial plan that assured competitive power.

"Also, Dresden is often referred to as the most important nuclear power station because of its size and type, and because on this job the plant owner, manufacturer and engineer-constructor developed the high degree of cooperation so essential to good performance on nuclear power projects.

"Although subsequently we worked with virtually all U. S. reactor manufacturers, Dresden really set the pattern."

Researching Peaceful Uses of Atomic Energy

General Electric was also the client on another project and in this case, the owner as well. Known as the Vallecitos Atomic Laboratory, it was located in central California not far from San Francisco. Here — in close collaboration with G-E — Bechtel designed and built a complex of facilities to develop peaceful applications of atomic energy. Among its functions this research center conducted studies and tests to obtain operational data for the Dresden plant. Components of the center were a developmental boiling water reactor, a critical experiment laboratory and a radioactive materials facility known as the "hot lab."

"Fossil-Fueled" Generating Units

The rise of nuclear power caused a fresh term to be introduced in the power industry — "fossil-fueled" — differentiating between conventional coal, oil or gas-fired generating stations and the new plants in which steam is heated by nuclear energy. Lively business continued for Bechtel in this older type of steam-electric facility; between 1955 and 1959 the Power and Industrial Division received contracts for 22 units, representing nearly four million kilowatts of new generating capacity.

Pipeline Projects Spanned the Globe

The period was also one of substantial activity in pipelines worldwide. In Canada the Trans Mountain oil pipeline was expanded, and that country's first major natural gas pipeline — the 800-mile Westcoast Transmission system — was designed and constructed under Bechtel management. The company provided the basic plan and built several sections of the 2300-mile Trans-Canada natural gas pipeline from Alberta to the populous industrial cities of eastern Canada. In the United States it took a prominent part in expansion of the Tennessee Gas Transmission system and other pipeline developments of the time. And to open a new U. S. market for Canadian gas, design was in progress and preparations were being made as 1960 approached to manage construction of a 1400-mile natural gas pipeline from Alberta to San Francisco Bay.

Overseas, Bechtel increased Trans-Arabian's capacity, completed a very difficult jungle pipeline in a second visit to Sumatra, and was taking part in the development of North African petroleum resources by engineering and constructing pipelines, terminals and attendant facilities in Algeria, Tunisia and Libya. Important as these activities were, another facet of the company's work in petroleum and natural gas transportation attracted more interest because of its impact on the whole economy of Western Europe.

The Trans-European Pipeline Study

In 1956 a group of international oil companies retained the Bechtel organization to investigate the economics and other implications of a Trans-European oil pipeline system. The result was a comprehensive study followed by a concise 20-page report (supported by an imposing compilation of data) which found such a pipeline system feasible, recommended the routes and estimated the capital and operating costs, earnings and return on investment. Completed in four months by experienced teams of staff specialists, the study's basic findings have been proved eminently sound by subsequent developments. George Colley sponsored and directed the work, with top-level support from Clark Rankin and Bob Bridges.

The Pipelines Were Built

Soon thereafter two pipelines in the over-all program proposed by the report were constructed — one, the Rotterdam-Rhine, under Bechtel's management. Early in the 1960's a third crude oil pipeline, similar

A jungle pipeline, road and deepwater terminal built in Sumatra in 1957-'58 proved to be one of the toughest jobs in Bechtel pipelining history. Problems of terrain, weather and even a civil war, made life difficult for the construction men.

By summer of the second year the new facilities were in operation and loading of the first tanker began on July 15.

to but not identical with the biggest envisioned by the 1956 study, was designed and managed by Bechtel-sponsored joint ventures.

This was the South European system, described in a subsequent chapter, which connects the Marseille area on the Mediterranean Sea with Strasbourg and Karlsruhe in the industrial heartland. Also during the 1960's, another pipeline — the Rhine-Danube — was the company's engineering-management responsibility. While not part of the originally recommended scheme, the Rhine-Danube project was an extension of it and would connect the South European system with the later Transalpine pipeline, linking the Adriatic Sea with Bavaria. Transalpine was completed under Bechtel's management in 1967.

Refineries Followed

Like the Trans Mountain pipeline across the Canadian Rockies to the Pacific Northwest, construction of the Western European pipelines inspired the building of new refineries. Again, as with the three refineries in Washington State that followed Trans Mountain, the company designed and built several grass-roots plants. Within the organization all this was looked upon as showing the value of studies in creating subsequent business opportunities, because the 1956 Trans-European pipeline study had started the chain reaction. This was true but perhaps the more significant aspects were the recognition implicit in the invitation to conduct this particular study and the high level of competence shown by its quality, accuracy, and prompt completion.

A Worldwide Hotels Program

In something of a departure from its established project fields, the company was invited to apply its experience and knowledge of laws, customs and conditions in a score of countries to a worldwide hotels construction program. The rapid growth of international travel had encouraged Pan American World Airways through its Intercontinental Hotels subsidiary to undertake a global chain of deluxe accommodations. Pan Am's chairman, Juan Trippe, has said many times that rising demand will require many more rooms as the years go on.

A conversation in 1957 between Trippe and S. D. Bechtel disclosed the air line's concern over delays and the mounting costs of its foreign

88

Examples of Bechtel management for overseas commercial building projects include many hotels such as the Southern Cross in Melbourne (above) and the Geneva and Frankfurt Intercontinentals.

construction. Both agreed that what was needed was an internationally experienced organization able to bring into the hotels program a sense of timing and budget control. As a result, an arrangement was made on a project basis which later evolved into a continuing relationship.

This service proved well suited to the program's needs. The client accomplished the desired ends of having the hotels completed on time at reasonable costs and was able to get reliable estimates on which to base financing for future projects. By 1967, 22 Intercontinental hotels were under construction or had been completed in 14 countries under this arrangement, among them such well-recognized houses as the Intercontinentals in Geneva, Vienna, Frankfurt and Karachi, and the Southern Cross in Melbourne. Success led to similar responsibilities for other clients and the company's business in hotels has expanded steadily. At the end of 1967 more than 5000 rooms had been built under Bechtel's project management and 4000 more were under construction.

Australia and New Zealand — the Melbourne Office

Before the Southern Cross Hotel was completed in Melbourne, Bechtel had established an office in that city as headquarters for its operations in Australia and New Zealand, thus extending its activities to another continental area. That part of the world was first opened to the company in 1955 with an on-site investigation of geothermal power potentialities in New Zealand. Early work in Australia involved two petrochemical plants, awarded in 1959. These were followed in succeeding years by hydroelectric, steam power, refinery and pipeline projects — and in 1967, by one of the world's largest iron ore developments.

As the Decade Closed

In the 1959 holiday season as a very busy decade neared an end, Steve Bechtel looked back over the organization's 60 active years, and particularly its 20 years overseas. He could count some 2000 projects completed in 30 countries on six continents, and at home in 40 states.

"Names such as Feather River, Hoover Dam, Bay Bridge, Calship, Marinship, Aramco, Tapline, Orinoco, Aden, Joppa, Dresden, and many others evoke memories of people and experiences from which we have learned much," he wrote.

But the end of a decade was also a time for looking ahead. In coming years, he continued, "our organization will be led more and more by younger men, many of whom have spent their entire business and professional lives with us.

"They have developed outstanding abilities and as they assume leadership, our future is assured by their strength and enthusiasm. They will continue to benefit from the experience and judgment of those of us who have had these responsibilities for many years. With genuine pleasure we contemplate the outlook with an organization which has never been stronger, under management that is seasoned and able — all with an esprit de corps that will make the years ahead busy, effective and happy."

El Segundo Steam Station, California. These four units were designed and constructed over a ten-year period.

CHAPTER SIX

Second Generation Fulfillment: 1960

For Bechtel, the year 1960 began like any other — work going on around the clock which meant around the globe in many time zones. But 1960 held special meaning for this business family, as matters turned out, because it would be the last under the leadership of second generation Stephen D. Bechtel. Additionally, the busy 1950's had ended; a new decade as well as a new order was at hand.

The World in 1960

What was happening in the outside world will serve as a reference to this point in time. In the United Kingdom the Conservatives were rounding out ten years in power under Churchill, Eden and MacMillan. In France, de Gaulle, in his second year as president, sought a solution for the massive settlers' revolt in Algeria. The Benelux economic and trade union countries of Belgium, The Netherlands and Luxembourg were establishing the pattern for closer cooperation by the Common Market six, which they had been instrumental in organizing. Under Adenauer, West Germany already had regained a position second only to the United States among western industrial nations. Australia and New Zealand were setting production records, attaining Gross National Products of $14 billions and $3.2 billions respectively. Canada, with population grown to 18 millions, had raised its output by two-thirds in a single decade, making it the sixth largest industrial country. And in the United States, John F. Kennedy, 43, had just been elected President.

GNP: $500 Billions

Businessmen remember 1960 for the recession that started during the summer and carried over into the next year. Downturn or not, the nation's total output passed the $500-billion level for the first time. In

93

that year nearly all industries in the western countries increased their expenditures for plant and equipment. The U. S. total amounted to almost $36 billions, up nearly 10 per cent over 1959.

Overseas, industrial construction gained momentum, especially in Western Europe, North Africa and Australia. New projects were getting bigger and more venturesome, notably in chemicals, electric power and the development of mineral ores and other raw materials. Energy use, on the increase everywhere, was building demand for petroleum products, natural gas and electric power, and the facilities for their production, processing and transportation.

Bechtel: Volume Quadrupled

The Bechtel business followed a well charted course, maintaining the rate of growth set in the preceding decade. Revenues in 1960 were more than twice those of 1955 and some four times the 1950 figure. There were nearly 4000 non-manual, salaried employees. Employee productivity had improved. It is likely that bigger projects and better organization were mainly responsible, but the widening use of such newer techniques as design models, critical path scheduling and computer assistance to engineering and administrative operations were having good effects, as well.

In retrospect, it was clear that Bechtel had come a long way in ten years. During a single decade the company had established itself as a top-ranking engineer-constructor in all of its fields. It had enlarged its in-house capabilities in various work-related areas of science. It had recognized and acted on opportunities at early stages in the expansion and modernization programs of the petroleum, chemical, power, mining and metallurgical industries. And in a pioneering joint effort with two associated engineering firms, it was preparing studies for the world's first truly contemporary urban rapid transit system — another important field of the future.

Those were some of the highlights. There were numerous other facets in the evolution of the company's 1950 staff into the larger, more diversified, more competent organization of 1960. For one thing, the dollar volume, number and variety of overseas jobs had expanded enormously and growth of the international business was continuing.

Peach Bottom Nuclear Power Station, Pennsylvania. First to use a graphite-moderated, helium-cooled reactor, it is one of the most advanced and economical nuclear power plants of its time.

Big Rock Point Nuclear Power Station, Michigan. One of three plants designed and built by Bechtel under fixed price, turn-key contracts at an early stage in the development of nuclear power.

In Power, 11 Million Kilowatts

For another, there was a great amount of power work. During the 13 years 1947-'60 Bechtel was responsible for fossil-fueled steam-electric generating capacity of 8.7 million kilowatts in 93 units. Its nuclear power figure then stood at 350,000 kilowatts and the hydroelectric total at over 1.7 millions — altogether some 11 million kilowatts, installed or under way. And much more was ahead.

Nuclear Power Plants at Fixed Prices

By 1960 the pacesetting nuclear power plant, Dresden, had been joined on the company's job roster by three others — Peach Bottom Unit 1 near Delta, Pennsylvania; Humboldt Bay Unit 3 at Eureka, California and Big Rock Point near Charlevoix, Michigan. Bechtel took full-responsibility contracts to deliver each of these projects for a fixed price. This decision required real courage at such an early point in the commercial application of atomic energy but it showed management's enthusiasm for the new medium and solid confidence in the company's nuclear power organization.

Peach Bottom was to prove a costly experience. Results at Humboldt Bay and Big Rock Point were excellent. Importantly, the tender of a firm price enabled these plant owners to obtain clearances, arrange financing and move into construction with minimum risk and maximum speed. Further, among engineer-constructors it put Bechtel in front at the outset, showing, incidentally, that all its know-how in nuclear power was not on the technical side.

The Scientific Development Department

Formation of the Scientific Development Department in 1958 under Perry Yates' sponsorship grew, in part, from the company's nuclear power activities. Many of the department's senior staff came from the Atomic Energy Commission's technical organization or otherwise had backgrounds in the nuclear sciences. But the program for this new operation was broad, intended to reach into any scientific field with actual or potential benefits for the company's work.

As time passed and experience deepened in utilizing the department's special talents, its work was directed toward acquiring early

Carol Project, Labrador, as originally completed. Now capable of producing 10-million long tons per year of pelletized concentrates, Carol is one of the world's largest iron ore beneficiation facilities.

competence in new areas of technology, and centralizing and coordinating Bechtel's capabilities in applied research, development and advanced engineering. Assignments included the design of NASA's Apollo Space Simulation Chambers at Houston, other space program responsibilities, studies and engineering projects in nuclear power and nuclear processes, saline water conversion and waste water treatment, air and water pollution, energy conversion, and underseas systems. In concept and practice, Bechtel's Scientific Development Department was — and is — absolutely unique among engineer-constructors.

Flourishing Times in Mining and Metals

The company's success in electric power was paralleled in metals. In view of the subsequent volume in this field, especially in the iron, steel, aluminum and copper industries, management's foresighted decision to emphasize this type of work proved timely and fortunate. Actually, a new era was commencing in some of the metals industries, brought about by recently developed or improved recovery processes, new equipment and larger, more economical plants. By 1960 Bechtel was in the thick of it.

A big Canadian engineering-management job launched in that year was the Carol Project in western Labrador. One of the largest iron ore beneficiation plants anywhere, it processed 15 million long tons of ore annually with 37-38 per cent iron content into more than 7½ million long tons of 66 per cent iron concentrate.

Carol went into operation in the summer of 1962. The particles of iron concentrate are too fine for direct use as blast furnace feed so they must be agglomerated into clusters at the steel mill or supplied in compressed pellet form. Consequently, in the following year a highly automated pelletizing plant was added to the Carol beneficiation complex. Then, in 1965-'66, a magnetic separation plant was constructed to recover an additional 650,000 long tons per year from the main plant's tailings. Subsequent programs increased the capacities of the concentrator and pelletizing plant each to 10 million long tons annually.

Urban Rapid Transit, Metropolitan Necessity

Another field Bechtel entered in the 1950's was urban rapid transit.

Metropolitan transit is enjoying revitalization after 50 years of comparative inactivity. Here, too, fresh concepts, new equipment and automation play important roles. The goal is a speedy, comfortable, economical alternative to traffic congestion, able to compete with the private automobile on its own terms. But modern rapid transit will take time to develop. A new transit system makes profound changes in its region, has social and political impact and costs a very substantial sum.

Biggest, Most Advanced Rapid Transit Program

Bechtel received a truly major assignment in its home office area through a joint venture formed with Parsons, Brinckerhoff, Quade & Douglas of New York and Tudor Engineering Company of San Francisco. The backgrounds of the three firms complemented one another, together they were experienced in all types of engineering required for planning and project administration of a major transit system. In 1959 a state-created regional body, the Bay Area Rapid Transit District (locally known at BART) authorized the joint venture to develop a basic plan for submission to the governing boards of counties on both sides of San Francisco Bay and, if approved by these boards, to the voters.

In the summer of 1961, on the basis of engineering data, preliminary design and estimates prepared by the joint venture, BART submitted the proposed system to the county governments. In November, 1962, voters of the three counties, San Francisco, Alameda and Contra Costa, approved a $792-million bond issue for a 75-mile system. Shortly thereafter, the District retained the joint venture, under Bechtel sponsorship, to do the detail engineering and to manage construction.

In addition to the bond financing, aggregate costs, then expected to total something over $1 billion, were to be met by $180 millions allocated from Bay Bridge automobile tolls for an underwater crossing, and $73 millions in revenue bonds for the rolling stock. Federal funds of $26 millions were obtained, in part for a test track and research program.

The project is by far the largest and most advanced urban transit venture yet undertaken and one of the biggest engineering and construction projects of its time. The total system includes 75 miles of special wide-gauge track; 16 miles of subway; a four-mile double tube beneath the Bay; three-and-a-half-mile twin tunnels through the Berkeley Hills;

25 miles of aerial line; 37 passenger stations; a headquarters building and central control station; and the necessary rolling stock, control, communications, power and maintenance facilities.

"BART will offer computer-run, interior-decorated commuting," reported the Wall Street Journal. "Unlike San Francisco's famed cable cars, BART can't survive by being quaint." The cars will be air conditioned and carpeted, with automobile-type seats. Trains will run at speeds of up to 80 miles per hour, will average some 50 mph including stops, and depart as often as every 90 seconds.

The National Society of Professional Engineers selected BART as the outstanding engineering project in the United States in 1967. (Second place went to the launching of the combined space vehicle — Apollo IV and its power supply, Saturn V.) The engineers cited the BART system as "a planned attempt to deal constructively with the need for public transportation in congested areas and to overcome the structural and economic difficulties involved."

President Lyndon B. Johnson launched the construction program in June, 1964, at a ceremony near the system's Concord terminus. Three and a half years later more than two-thirds of the total mileage was under construction.

By 1967, estimated costs to complete the project had exceeded the forecast made five years earlier by some $150 millions. An amount of $190 millions had been set up originally for inflation and contingency. But this proved inadequate to cover a delay caused by a taxpayer's suit, the upgrading of plans, changes and additions demanded by some communities as the price for local clearances and above all, rapid inflation and escalation in construction costs. A major factor was an increase of over 30 per cent in area labor rates since 1960. All this created a serious financial problem but one that every big project of long duration was having at the time, and for which solutions would be found.

District officials are confident that when operational, the system will meet with enthusiastic public response. They predict it will carry half of the area's heavy peak-hour commuter traffic. The BART program — like so many Bechtel projects over the years — is a pacesetting development, paving the way for future rapid transit systems everywhere.

S. D. Bechtel and prototype car for the new rapid transit system.

Landscaped linear parkway and award-winning elevated structure of Bay Area Rapid Transit District blends harmoniously with its environment.

Interior, BART car.

Bechtel executives and their wives visited the BART project during construction—(left) John Kiely and Ed Garbarini; (right) Rudy Grammater and Charlie Draney.

Bechtel Studies — Where Great Projects Begin

The Bay Area Rapid Transit program began with technical and economic studies. During the 1950's the Bechtel organization greatly stepped up investigative work of this kind. By 1960 its capabilities were being employed to determine the feasibility and optimum program for a wide range of undertakings. As Jerry Komes said:

"Studies are important to us for a variety of reasons — some because they show our technical competence and the way it is utilized in the service of clients, and others because they lead to important projects or expose new fields of activity, rich with promise for the future."

The far-reaching results of the 1956 study for a Trans-European pipeline have been described. Various others have preceded decisions of major import, frequently for developments of a pioneer nature. Examples include the first commercial plant to extract oil from the vast Canadian tar sands deposits, and the biggest, most significant sea water conversion program yet conceived, both projects of the 1960's.

A highly important new field of fuel supply was involved in a group of related studies initiated in 1958, which resulted nine years later in a comprehensive facilities program for the liquefaction and transportation of natural gas from Alaska to Japan. The principals are two U. S. oil companies and two Japanese utilities. Natural gas, surplus to Alaska's needs, will be liquefied at a plant on the Kenai peninsula and transported to Japan in special tankers for regasification and use. The supply operation calls for annual deliveries of 139 million cubic feet per day. In addition to the studies, Bechtel is responsible for design and construction of the liquefaction facilities in Alaska and is serving as consultant on regasification and liquid storage in Japan.

A Texas-to-New York natural gas transmission system and Western Europe's first major natural gas pipeline network grew out of Bechtel studies, as did one of the world's largest hydroelectric projects on which construction has begun in Labrador. Studies preceded the Upper American River 11-year hydro program, the Carol iron ore beneficiation project and various grass-roots petroleum and chemical complexes. In addition, there have been studies of a unifying highway through the Arab countries, a Suez pipeline, a plan for massive chemical fertilizer production in India and other developments with potentialities of world import.

A company-wide survey in the 1960's counted more than 300 Bechtel studies completed in a three-year period and several thousand over all — forerunners of many great projects and altogether a tremendous store of information, some of which reaches out to new frontiers of engineering-construction knowledge.

The Channel Tunnel Study

A tunnel beneath the English Channel has intrigued heads of government, engineers and financiers for more than 150 years, so perhaps it was inevitable that Bechtel with two joint venture associates should become involved in this challenging possibility. Napoleon, among others, was seriously interested in such an undersea link between England and France. In 1880 construction was actually started, then halted. Since then, various problems have prevented agreement. In the late 1950's, with continuing growth of the Western European economy, conditions appeared more favorable.

Bechtel, Brown & Root, and Morrison-Knudsen combined their respective capabilities in 1959 to make a technical study and provide the basic design, a cost estimate and construction schedule. Their objective was a tunnel that could handle the indicated traffic well into the future, capable of being completed on a short schedule at lowest cost. Technical Studies, Inc., of New York authorized the work, acting for The Channel Tunnel Study Group, a consortium of British, French and American interests of which Technical Studies is the U. S. member.

The resulting plan proposes two single-track railroad tunnels through which automobiles riding "piggyback" on special flatcars, as well as other freight and passengers in conventional rail vehicles, would be transported by shuttle trains operating at frequent intervals. The design provides transport capacity of more than twice the volume of traffic forecast for the year 1980.

A major feature is the proposal to bore the tunnels through chalk deposits located by subsurface exploration and thought to exist along the entire route. The chalk is structurally strong and essentially impervious to water. Most important and the key to the joint venture's construction planning—the chalk lends itself well to excavation by "moles," efficient rotating machines that make a cross-section cut the full diameter of the excavation. The tunnel would then be lined with concrete.

The recommended program, the engineers believe, is not only the best and most economical of the alternatives considered, but would minimize the estimated time of construction by a full year under that required for any other type of crossing.

Since the study's completion, the French and British governments have conducted joint investigations and published a report incorporating many features of the program developed by Bechtel, Brown & Root, and Morrison-Knudsen for The Channel Study Group. A memorandum was issued to interested parties inviting basic plans for "contracting" the project, in which financing was a major consideration. From the replies received, three organizations, including The Channel Tunnel Study Group, were selected in 1967 to submit proposals.

The next step — expected to be a joint decision by the two governments to proceed and award of the project to the winning consortium — is awaited with keen interest. Whatever the outcome, the American joint venture engineering study has made a major contribution to the eventual realization of this important development.

Answering Questions of Probability

A facet in Bechtel's evolving reputation that had become clearly established by 1960 was its affinity for imaginative, trail-blazing jobs. As projects grew more ambitious, this situation was closely related to the company's study capabilities. Such undertakings often require immense capital expenditures involving questions of probability, for which reliable answers must be found in advance of commitment.

From Study to 1400-Mile Pipeline — the Alberta-California Project

In this context a notably big job, the Alberta-California natural gas pipeline completed in 1961, was the end-product of planning which began five years earlier. The project itself exemplified the advantage offered by a complete technical service under single responsibility. The pipeline was 1400-miles long, 36 inches in diameter and cost $300 millions. Construction of the basic system began in October, 1960, and was completed some 14 months later in a straight-through operation. The project was managed by its designers, from the line's origin in Alberta to the California-Oregon border. During peak activity six major contractors and more than 4400 men were at work simultaneously.

Built primarily to serve Northern and Central California for which, in its initial operating period, deliveries averaged 415 million cubic feet of gas per day, it also provided 152 million cubic feet daily to Pacific Northwest customers and 36 million cubic feet per day to a Montana utility. Bechtel subsequently participated in expanding the system by the design and installation of additional pumping capacity.

Not All Smooth Sailing

This story has been confined to the broader aspects of Bechtel's development with the result that it may give the impression of an unbroken succession of engineering triumphs. Such was not the case. Along the way there were difficulties, mistakes and losses.

The less-than-happy jobs have been but a small fraction of the whole, but when one does occur the company's management reviews the circumstances, digests the findings and lays out guidelines for the future.

One example goes back some 30 years. A joint venture consisting of Bechtel and some of the other firms then coming off the world-acclaimed Hoover Dam project, ran into serious difficulty on a major highway tunnel. Cave-ins, delays and costly extra construction piled trouble on trouble, compounded by a bid that was too low in the first place.

As work progressed it became apparent that geological conditions at the site were much more difficult than the contractors anticipated, although they were experienced in this type of work and recognized some of the uncertainties. Fresh from the success at Hoover Dam, it is likely that they discounted the problems, feeling that momentum and hard work would see them through.

In any event the highway tunnel was the biggest disappointment any of the group had experienced up to that time. It taught them to realistically consider all factors in a major risk project and that difficulties must have a proportionate and proper contract price or the bidder will be in trouble.

That is what happened on the tunnel job. All in all, the hard lessons learned there were invaluable as the years went on.

More recently the firm suffered a substantial loss on a large natural

The Alberta-California natural gas pipeline under construction over the Continental Divide at Flathead Ridge, British Columbia, elevation 7200 feet, the highest point on the 1400-mile route.

Pulling the 2200-foot crossing of the Pend Oreille River in Idaho.

Alberta-California system: pipelaying on the steep walls of Juniper Canyon, Oregon, required special construction techniques.

Looking into a length of 36-inch pipe are S. D. Bechtel Jr., Norman Sutherland, president of Pacific Gas and Electric, and S. M. Blair, Canadian Bechtel's president.

Inspection party traveled to the project in a company plane—a regular Bechtel practice.

gas treatment and sulfur recovery plant. Although a separate job and for a different client, the plant was closely related operationally to one of Bechtel's most important natural gas pipeline projects which was rapidly nearing completion, so time was a vital consideration. Therefore when the company was asked to submit figures only a short period was permitted for preparing the bid, and for designing and building the gas treatment plant. Engineering began in March and the facility was operating in January of the following year.

Sulfur recovery from natural gas in such big volume — this was the world's largest plant — posed problems that Bechtel did not properly evaluate in meeting the tight bid deadline. Located in a region of severe winters, much of the plant had to be built during extremely bad weather.

The hastily prepared estimate, together with the tight schedule and bitter weather, hurt the project badly. On the plus side, the final plant proved outstanding. Its design incorporated many innovations, all of which were effective, and the operation has been entirely successful.

Over its long business life the company has suffered financial losses on several other projects, one of the most severe being the previously mentioned first unit of the Peach Bottom Nuclear Power Station. Here, as prime contractor, Bechtel had a fixed price agreement covering both its own services and a manufacturer-furnished steam supply system. This, a helium-cooled reactor, was the first of its type for commercial use.

The contract was made in the late 1950's at a time of great stress in the competition between public and private development of the gas-cooled reactor. Bechtel accepted the manufacturer's representations with reference to the state of development of this particular gas-cooled concept and with some concern, agreed to a fixed price for the project. It turned out that gas-cooled reactors had many unknowns and a succession of difficulties with the steam supply system delayed operation of the station for a long period. Despite these problems Bechtel believed the gas-cooled process to be fundamentally sound. In addition, the owner had been joined in a support program by 52 other utilities, all of which were interested in the outcome.

The project turned out to be extremely expensive to the engineer-constructor. After several substantial changes the plant went into operation successfully and proved the viability of the process and design. Having perfected the reactor in this prototype installation, its eventual success ironically benefited the reactor manufacturer more than Bechtel. But as some Bechtelites said, that was the "rub of the green." There were some pleasant consequences, however. The owner selected the company to engineer and build follow-on nuclear units two and three, and since then, a number of the utilities involved in financing Peach Bottom's first unit have awarded Bechtel several large new plants on their own power systems.

Repeat Clients and "Sweetheart Accounts"

Most of Bechtel's customers are the major firms in basic industries — oil, natural gas, chemicals, power, metals and so on — the blue chip international companies in each field. As a group they represent a substantial part of world production in their respective industries and big potential business for an engineer-constructor but — and this is the key point—they are few in number. Therefore it is necessary to obtain a steady flow of work from the same sources, in short, to keep clients happy. The company is closely attuned to this reality, as shown by its healthy repeat business volume from regular customers, which represents more than 85 per cent of its total business.

Some of the biggest customers became what Steve called "sweetheart accounts."

"We worked hard to get really close to certain major companies," he said, "which made it possible for us to work very effectively with their managements.

"We believed this close working relationship would benefit both parties — and it has. Clients find that there are important advantages in having projects designed and built by an organization that fully understands their particular requirements."

Career Employees; the Bechtel Service Awards

In his final year as president, the senior Steve headed an organization that was quite different from the construction contracting business he had joined 40 years before.

One point of difference was that a great many employees at all levels were finding lifetime careers with Bechtel. In 1966, when the Service Award Program was inaugurated, some 1150 received the silver emblem representing 10 or more years with the company and 350 the gold emblem for 20 years or more. These numbers were remarkably high for the construction industry.

Consultants: the Importance of Experience

A policy initiated before World War II by the senior Steve and continued under Steve Jr., has proved very effective in adding to the organization's strength. This is the practice of selectively retaining a substantial number of consultants.

Of this program, S. D. Bechtel recently said:

"Distinguished scientists, engineers and administrators are consultants to our several divisions at home and abroad. Numbering more than 120, these people are readily available and used to the maximum benefit of our projects. They bring us the seasoned judgment which comes only from many years of accomplishment.

"It is our practice to establish consulting boards composed of men chosen for special eminence in the fields of activity most applicable to a given project. Our consulting boards meet regularly, not only to review plans and designs before construction begins but also to make periodic trips to judge the implementation of plans, construction practices and results in the field. The boards then report back to our senior executives, giving us the benefit of independent judgment and opinion. Having no direct responsibilities for operations, our consultants can and do provide a totally objective viewpoint.

"Another result of our consultants' activity is the inspiring effect they have on our operating men. Staff people strengthen their backgrounds and benefit in many ways from association with these men of proven eminence.

"Conversely, a number of our consultants have commented on how stimulating and rewarding it is to continue to be identified with younger operating men who have the responsibility for great engineering works around the world.

"Consultants are an important and appreciated part of our organization and a great asset."

Recognition

Straws in the wind, perhaps, but in 1960 and during the preceding decade the growing stature of the Bechtel organization was reflected in yet another way — through recognition accorded its senior executives.

In 1950, S. D. Bechtel had been elected to membership in the Business Advisory Council, later renamed The Business Council. This top-level group of major corporation executives, numbering some 60 active members, consult together in the national interest and by invitation with the President, members of the Cabinet and other key officials of Government. Steve completed two years as chairman of The Business Council and, on reaching retirement age in 1965, became a graduate member.

S. D. Bechtel's Civic Activities

He was appointed by President Eisenhower in 1954 to the President's Advisory Committee on a National Highway Program, the compact five-man body chaired by General Lucius Clay, which studied and reported on a nationwide interstate highway plan. Involving urban and suburban relationships as well, this report is the base on which the present $50-billion 15-year interstate highway system is being built — the largest transportation program ever conceived.

For many years Steve was a trustee of Stanford University and remains a vitally interested and active director of the Stanford Research Institute. In 1960 he was elected to the Board of Trustees of the Ford Foundation. In addition, he has been chairman of the San Francisco Bay Area Council, a regional development body; trustee of the Committee for Economic Development; consultant to the National Security Council; is a senior member of the National Industrial Conference Board; and a participant in other well-known civic and national organizations.

Corporate Directorships

The business world recognized his special qualities by election to the directorates of several leading corporations, notably Continental Can Corporation, Industrial Indemnity Company, Morgan Guaranty Trust Company, Pacific Gas Transmission Company, Southern Pacific Company and United States Lines Company. In recent years he has been phasing out many of these activities.

Honors

The academic world, as well as Steve's colleagues in engineering-construction, a foreign government and the Holy See have honored him. In 1951 he received the Achievement Award of the Building Industry Conference Board of San Francisco. In the following year, he was given the Moles Award (New York) for outstanding achievement in construction and later, the Golden Beaver Award for Management by The Beavers, a western construction recognition group. The University of California Alumni Association chose him as "Alumnus of the Year" in 1952. Honorary Degrees of LL.D. were conferred by the University of California in 1954, Loyola University of Los Angeles in 1958 and University of the Pacific in 1966. He has been decorated with the Order of the Cedar of Lebanon (1956) and made a Knight of the Order of St. Sylvester Pope (1956). Forbes Magazine selected him in 1957 as one of "America's Fifty Foremost Business Leaders." In 1960 he was chosen by the U. S. Joint Chiefs of Staff to receive the National Defense Transportation Award, "in support of national security."

In 1960, also, came the particular recognition that to one of Steve Bechtel's calling has perhaps the greatest meaning — the John Fritz Medal Award. Named for a turn-of-the-century pioneer in steelmaking, the award is given for "notable scientific or industrial achievement" by representatives of the four national engineering societies (as of that time), the American Society of Civil Engineers, American Institute of Mining, Metallurgical and Petroleum Engineers, The American Society of Mechanical Engineers, and American Institute of Electrical Engineers. The citation read:

"Stephen Davison Bechtel — engineer, builder, industrialist and leader of broad vision in large construction undertakings nationally and internationally; a pioneer in the creation of the modern construction industry, which is unequalled throughout the world and which has made possible the pre-eminence of our country in time of war and in time of peace."

S. D. Bechtel Jr. in Community and National Affairs

Steve Jr.'s activities during the 1950's had been confined almost entirely to the Bechtel business, yet he also was entering into community service — in his home area on the Executive Board of the Piedmont Boy Scout Council and in San Francisco as a trustee of the California Academy of Sciences.

In subsequent years, even as he took over top responsibility for the company, his civic interests expanded. Soon these included active membership in The Business Council, membership for six years on the Advisory Council of the Stanford Graduate School of Business, and a vice chairmanship of the National Industrial Conference Board, of which he is also a senior member and trustee. He has been a trustee of the United Bay Area Crusade. His alma mater, Purdue, in 1964 selected him in the first group of 10 to receive its School of Engineering's "Distinguished Alumnus" award. And in 1967 he was elected to the Board of Trustees of the California Institute of Technology.

Steve Jr. received an important public service assignment in 1967 when President Johnson announced his appointment to a committee formed to study and recommend means for accelerating industry's participation in the redevelopment of slum areas. This group's recommendations were to provide the basis for later Congressional legislation. Steve Jr.'s colleagues on the committee included Edgar F. Kaiser, its chairman and a long-time Bechtel associate, John A. McCone, George Meany and Walter Reuther of the AFL-CIO, and others from the senior ranks of industry, labor and banking.

Further, the younger Steve was widening his business interests. By the mid-1960's he was a director of five outside corporations: Crocker-Citizens National Bank, Industrial Indemnity Company, Hanna Mining Company, Southern Pacific Company, and Tenneco, Inc.

Other Directors Were Active

In 1956 Kenneth Bechtel was elected president of the National Council, Boy Scouts of America, a position he held until 1959. The first far westerner and the first Boy Scout ever elected to that office, his elevation to Scouting's highest post was the culmination of 40 years of interest and service, commencing when he joined an Oakland troop as a boy in his teens. Kenneth has received virtually every honor that Scouting bestows. He is an honorary vice president of the National Council and a member of the Executive Board. A director of Wells Fargo Bank and

Congratulations were offered by Robert Gordon Sproul, president of the University of California, after conferring the honorary Doctor of Laws degree on S. D. Bechtel at the University's 91st Commencement, June 18, 1954.

Steve Jr. received his alma mater's "Distinguished Alumnus" award in 1964 from Dr. F. L. Hovde, president of Purdue University.

The John Fritz Medal and Certificate were presented to Steve by Col. E. R. Needles, chairman of the Board of Award, on behalf of the five major engineering societies.

a trustee of the California Academy of Sciences, he is or has been active in various other business, community and cultural organizations as a trustee or director.

Bill Waste was elected chairman of the San Francisco Bay Area Council in 1950, which he continued to serve for many years as a trustee. Among his numerous civic activities were presidencies of the San Francisco Post of the American Ordnance Society and of the Stock Exchange Club, and memberships on the Boards of the San Francisco Chamber of Commerce, the Menninger Foundation, Franklin Hospital, the San Francisco Branch of the American Cancer Society and the Commonwealth Club of California. Bill has been president of the Marin Council and a member of the Regional Executive Committee, Region XII, Boy Scouts of America.

Perry Yates' outside interests have been mainly concerned with educational and professional matters. He is chairman of the University of California's Engineering Advisory Council. In the mid-1960's, under Perry's chairmanship, an important task force of the Council studied and reported to the University on long-term requirements and future directions for engineering education. He has been a director of The Beavers and continues, after many years, on the Board of the Pacific Coast Electrical Association.

While with Bechtel, John L. Simpson was honored by the University of California and by two foreign governments for his contributions to international understanding. He has taken a leading role in world affairs organizations and served as president of the World Affairs Council of Northern California in the late 1950's. In 1959, King Baudouin of Belgium awarded him the decoration of Officer of the Order of Leopold II. France, in 1960, conferred the Legion of Honor on John Simpson, and in that year, as well, he received the honorary degree of Doctor of Laws from the University of California.

Others in Bechtel management were active in professional and technical circles. As examples: John Kiely is a director of the Engineers Joint Council. J. N. Landis has been national president of The American Society of Mechanical Engineers and of the Engineers Joint Council, and chairman of the U. S. National Committee of the World Power Conference. S. M. Blair is president of the Canadian Nuclear Council.

116

W. K. Davis served two terms as president of the Atomic Industrial Forum. J. P. Buehler is chairman of the Technical Activities Committee of the American Society of Civil Engineers, and a member of the Executive Committee of the U. S. Committee on Large Dams.

The list could be greatly extended but the point has been made. The Bechtel organization's increasing stature was receiving acknowledgement through elections and awards to its executives by their peers in civic, academic, professional and industrial circles.

Bechtel as Corporate Citizen

As a corollary, these activities showed increasing awareness on Bechtel's part of its obligations as a corporate citizen. During most of its business lifetime the company has contributed to worthy causes but in the years following World War II and particularly during the 1950's and 1960's, this area of interest drew closer attention from management. In the United States the Bechtel Foundation, which receives its entire support from Bechtel Corporation, was established to handle gifts to approved charitable, health and educational institutions, and for the same purpose in Canada, the Bechtel Foundation of Canada was formed.

As overseas operations grew, the contributions program was extended to countries where area offices and long-term projects are located, consistent with policy in North America.

The personal participation of Bechtel's executives in civic and industrial activities has become a matter for additional study, particularly in the home office area, where large employment rolls and a new headquarters building create a special situation.

The Family's Role

For many years the Bechtel family, unobtrusively and often anonymously, has been active in the field of philanthropy. As individuals and through family foundations, the two Steves and their wives, and daughter Barbara and her husband Paul L. Davies Jr., have put a great deal of time, effort and substance into assisting carefully selected educational, community, social and cultural institutions. Only rarely is the name identified with the gift, understandable exceptions being the Bechtel Engineering Building at American University of Beirut,

Bechtel International Student Center at Stanford University, and Bechtel Hall residence and facilities for student nurses at Samuel Merritt Hospital in Oakland.

Kenneth Bechtel, in his characteristically quiet way, has given generously to many worthy programs.

Their contributions have largely gone unpublicized, so this side of the Bechtels is little known outside the family itself, but philanthropy is a matter to which they devote much serious thought.

Few Changes in Top Manpower

As 1960 moved into the late fall it appeared the year would bring little change in the alignment of senior management. In February Rudy Grammater had been elected to the Board and in June, John O'Connell. Otherwise, through November, there were no changes among the directors and officers.

More Action Just Below

There was more activity among members of the developing group. As examples, the circumstances of one vice president and eight who later would be named to that office showed that Bechtel was continuing to grow most of its own leaders.

In 1960 Harry Waste, who had been elected a vice president in 1958, became deputy manager of the Pipeline Division. In future years he would assume the division managership and further enlarge his responsibilities when all pipeline operations worldwide were centralized in the Pipeline Division.

In the Power and Industrial Division, Ike Caraco was appointed deputy manager of the Southern California office in 1960 and area manager in the following year. In 1962, he was elected vice president and with formation of the Vernon Division in 1966, became its manager.

The Zarzaitine-Mediterranean pipeline across Algeria and Tunisia occupied the attention of two International Division men in 1960. Jim Leaver and Glenn Buchanan were project manager and deputy, respectively. The next year, Buchanan was selected to manage the construction of overseas refineries and chemical plants, and in 1962 — his 21st year with Bechtel — Glenn was appointed resident manager in the

London office, which is European headquarters for that type of work. He was elected vice president in 1964.

Jim Leaver, a real veteran of Bechtel's work in the Arab countries, was placed in charge of Middle East and African projects in 1963, and in 1966, of oil field developments for the newly established International Petroleum and Chemical Division. He received a vice presidency in 1965.

After important refinery and chemical engineering assignments in San Francisco and London, Porter Thompson assumed prime responsibility for New York office operations in 1958, as manager of technical services. His election as vice president took place in 1964. Then in 1967, Thompson's duties were again increased when he returned to the home office as Refinery and Chemical's manager of operations.

Before 1960 Bob Cheatham had advanced to manager of industrial plant engineering in the Power and Industrial Division. Next, he was chosen to manage all of the division's San Francisco-based engineering activities, which included the Montreal and Washington engineering organizations. Cheatham received that appointment in 1963 and three years later, a vice presidency.

Three men who would be elected vice presidents in 1967 were, in this year of 1960, given added responsibilities which reflected the growth of their capabilities. S. Martin Akeyson Jr. had joined the organization originally at Calship and subsequently worked up through the company's power and industrial construction activities. In 1960 he was named manager of services for that division. Donald R. Ferguson, another former Calshipper, having just completed a tour of duty as project engineer of the grass-roots Hawaiian Refinery, received additional assignments which soon were followed by his appointment as assistant chief engineer in the Refinery and Chemical Division at San Francisco. In that division, also, Jacob Lindenbaum — whose first Bechtel work had been on the war-emergency Canol Project — was appointed manager of refinery projects.

December 1960: Third Generation President — S. D. Bechtel Jr.

The year 1960 entered its final month. Then, on the second day, came the event Stephen D. Bechtel had awaited with hope and pleasurable anticipation for nearly four decades — the election by the Board of

Stephen D. Bechtel Jr. to the presidency of Bechtel Corporation.

"This recognition of ability and leadership," the senior Steve said to all members of the organization, "is a logical and thoughtfully considered step in the development of our company.

"Steve worked first in the Bechtel business as a student engineer many years ago on the Oakland Port of Embarkation project. His early full-time duties were on pipeline construction in the field. Since then he has been increasingly part of the management of the company's activities in some twenty states and a number of foreign countries. For several years he has been our senior officer for the international, pipeline, financial and equipment divisions. His new position is a natural development and one which further strengthens our executive management.

"Our operations have continued to expand and while my functions as chairman will remain unchanged, Steve's assumption of the presidency will enable me to concentrate to a greater degree on major policy, long-range planning and client relationships.

"The modification of senior executive functions — that of having a chairman and president — is another important step forward for the Bechtel organization. This assures continuity of our traditions and lays the foundation for even greater progress in the years ahead."

An era was closing. It represented a business lifetime of accomplishment, a 40-year period during which the senior Steve's foresight, vigor and strong direction, with able and loyal assistance from his associates, created a truly great international professional and business organization, the largest and most diversified in its industry, unique among major engineer-constructors.

But actually there was no ending, no beginning, merely an orderly transition, for continuity is a Bechtel hallmark. The younger president took charge at once. And he was well qualified to meet the still greater future demands of his office, as he would soon prove.

CHAPTER SEVEN

A New Generation Takes Over

This story has been mainly concerned with Bechtel activities under second generation leadership, particularly in the 1950's decade. But it would be grossly incomplete without at least the highlights of what happened thereafter. In fact, the accomplishments of that earlier active period were the forerunners of greater things to come.

When Stephen D. Bechtel Jr. assumed the presidency he had a balanced management team at his side. Numbering about 100 in 1960, this group represented a good mix of ages and talents, combining experience with enthusiasm, vigor and confidence. It included the Board of Directors, the vice presidents and some 75 managers and ranking supervisors.

Bechtel Corporation's Board of Directors

Bechtel Corporation's Board at that time consisted of S. D. Bechtel, chairman; S. D. Bechtel Jr., president and chairman of the Executive Committee; W. E. Waste and J. P. Yates, executive vice presidents; J. R. Kiely and J. W. Komes, senior vice presidents; R. D. Grammater and J. F. O'Connell, vice presidents; K. K. Bechtel, S. M. Blair, R. L. Bridges and J. L. Simpson.

Illustrative of the continuity in management that has been a company characteristic, two members of the 1960 Board (S. D. and K. K. Bechtel) had been directors of this and the earlier companies since the 1920's and four since the 1940's (W. E. Waste, J. P. Yates, R. L. Bridges and J. L. Simpson). Of the remaining directors, four had been elected in the 1950's (S. D. Bechtel Jr., J. R. Kiely, J. W. Komes and S. M. Blair) and two in 1960 (R. D. Grammater and J. F. O'Connell). During the first half of the succeeding decade the Board welcomed four others — C. T. Draney in 1961, E. J. Garbarini and Eugene Lippa in 1964, and W. S. Slusser in 1965. In 1967 two vacancies, occasioned by retirements, were filled by senior officers, as will be noted. So there continued to be an infusion of new blood, but Bechtel-typed, for all were men developed in the organization or closely associated with it for a long time.

Willis S. Slusser was a newcomer to the company's roster in 1964 when he was named vice president, counsel and secretary but like his colleagues and ex-partners, Bob Bridges and Mynderse Van Hoesen, he was an old hand in Bechtel service. As a member of the firm of Thelen, Marrin, Johnson and Bridges, the Corporation's legal counsel, Slusser had been closely associated with the company's affairs for many years.

Passing Time Brought Changes

In the normal course of advancing years, John L. Simpson resigned his directorship in 1961. W. E. Waste retired in 1963 from operational duties, remaining on the Board until 1967. In 1965 S. D. Bechtel resigned his Board chairmanship and was named senior director. In 1967 S. M. Blair retired from the Corporation's Board, and Vice Presidents R. A. Bowman and I. R. Caraco were elected directors. Earlier in the year J. R. Kiely and J. W. Komes had been appointed executive vice presidents. In September, J. F. O'Connell was elected senior vice president.

Two veterans of the war projects passed away during this period — Bill Ayers in 1964 and J. S. "Jumpy" Sides in 1966. Both had served ably and loyally for some 25 years, and their election to vice presidencies in 1953 has been noted. Ayers, ex-Marinship, was active in company administration. With growth and an increase in procurement activities he had concentrated on that phase of the business in later years. Sides, works manager at Calship, became Bechtel's eastern manager in New York during the early 1950's. Among his responsibilities he had charge of many large special projects, including the worldwide hotels program.

In November, 1967, W. H. Ness was killed in the crash of a jetliner near Cincinnati. Taken at the height of his powers, he was one of the mainstays of the executive structure as a vice president and the highly successful manager of business development, Power and Industrial Division. Blessed with a searching mind, keen sense of values and a penchant for hard work, Bill Ness was a fine team worker and a real contributor to the company's growth and effectiveness.

Seven Years of Robust Growth

Consistent with Bechtel's progress, by 1967 its senior management population had increased to over 200 worldwide, double the 1960 number. In the same period the non-manual staff had tripled — from 4000 to 12,000 — and the annual volume of new business had also tripled.

The Vice Presidents

The officers, other than directors, who held major responsibilities for operations at the close of 1967 numbered 19. The vice presidents were S. M. Akeyson Jr., division manager of business development, Mining & Metals Division; G. E. Buchanan, resident manager, European operations, International Petroleum & Chemical Division; J. P. Buehler, manager, Hydro & Transportation Division; R. A. Cheatham, division manager of engineering, Mining & Metals Division; J. H. Crispin, treasurer; W. K. Davis, manager of business development, International Power, Industrial and Metals Division; D. R. Ferguson, New York area manager of operations, Refinery & Chemical Division; L. J. Kelly, division manager of business development and process services, Refinery & Chemical Division; J. M. Leaver, division manager of oil field development, International Petroleum & Chemical Division; J. Lindenbaum, San Francisco area manager of operations, Refinery & Chemical Division; E. J. Mahoney Jr., manager of corporate business development; J. W. Merryman, manager of procurement; A. J. Orselli, division manager of power department, International Power, Industrial & Metals Division; Clark Rankin, manager, Europe and Middle East, Pipeline Division; K. O. Taylor, division manager of construction, Power & Industrial Division; P. E. Thompson, division operations manager, Refinery & Chemical Division; H. F. Waste, manager, Pipeline Division; J. M. Wellman, president, Wellman-Lord, Inc.; and B. F. Willson, president, Canadian Bechtel Limited.

Strong Additions to the Officers Group

All have appeared in this narrative at appropriate times and places along the way, except for four men who entered the organization in the 1960's. Three came between 1962 and 1965—L. J. Kelly, J. H. Crispin and B. F. Willson. The fourth, J. M. Wellman, joined in 1966 when his company was acquired by Bechtel, as will shortly appear.

Jack Kelly assumed his new duties as a Bechtel vice president after 25 years with another large refinery process, engineering and construction firm where he had important roles in developing processes and equipment now widely used in the petroleum industry. For his first five years at Bechtel he had charge of refinery and chemical engineering and thereafter of divisional business development and process services.

Hewes Crispin had risen to a senior administrative position with another major engineer-constructor before joining Bechtel. As vice president and treasurer he succeeded and reports to Vice President R. D. Grammater. With degrees in engineering and business administration and specialized experience in international operations, Crispin's background was well suited to his Bechtel responsibilities.

Bruce Willson came into the organization as president of Canadian Bechtel Limited and vice president of Bechtel Corporation. He succeeded Sid Blair in CBL's presidency when Blair, on reaching his mid sixties, was named CBL's vice chairman. Willson's election continued the Bechtel policy of providing Canadian leadership for its Canadian activities. A civil engineer and utilities executive, he was president of two Alberta gas distribution companies and vice president and director of the Province's main gas transmission firm prior to his affiliation with Bechtel.

The Directors' Advisory Group

As one consequence of growth the number of Bechtel management people steadily increased. Means were sought to give the company's top echelon direct access to the talents of these competent men.

Accordingly in 1964 the Directors' Advisory Group was formed. Its members were selected largely on the criteria of performance and leadership ability. The membership is rotated to include a broad segment of the upper management population. Familiarly known as DAG, the principal functions of this body are to furnish the directors, from independent points of view, with suggestions, advice and information, and through ad hoc committees to recommend solutions to assigned problems. Conversely, through meetings and discussions with the directors, DAG members are given a comprehensive understanding of important

The second largest U.S. gold producer and first major all-new gold mining operation in 25 years— the Carlin (Nevada) mine and cyanidation plant went into operation in 1965, with recovery capacity of 200,000 fine ounces of gold annually.

policies, activities and problems. In these and other ways the DAG program is aimed at further improving the company's communications, management capabilities and effectiveness. In addition to the vice presidents (other than directors), the active DAG participants number about 60, of whom some 40 were active members at the close of 1967. Their names appear in the Appendix.

Operating Divisions Increased to Eight

Consistent with its flexibility in adjusting organizational patterns to changing requirements, the company made an important realignment in the Spring of 1966. The four operating divisions were restructured into eight to accommodate growth and open the way for more complete utilization of experience and capabilities.

The Refinery and Chemical Division and the Pipeline Division remained as they were, but the latter was given worldwide responsibilities rather than in North America only, as in the past. The former Power and Industrial Division became four divisions, of which one retained the original title. The others are the Vernon Division, responsible for power and industrial projects in the U. S. Southwest and for urban planning and land developments worldwide; the Hydro Power and Transportation Division; and the Mining and Metals Division. The former International Division was divided into the International Power, Industrial and Metals Division, and the International Petroleum and Chemical Division which, like their predecessor, are operative in all parts of the world except the United States and its possessions, Canada and Mexico.

While each division's general sphere of activities is indicated by its title, in the best interest of the over-all program divisional lines are sometimes crossed — after topside approval.

Office of the President

At this time also, S. D. Bechtel Jr. announced the formation of a high level group called the Office of the President. In addition to the president, the members were — and are — J. P. Yates, executive vice president, deputy to S. D. Bechtel Jr. and senior officer in his absence; J. R. Kiely and J. W. Komes, executive vice presidents; J. F. O'Connell, senior vice president; and R. L. Bridges. The president's associates assist in

126

planning, coordination and control, and provide corporate management. The five company executives — S. D. Bechtel Jr., and Messrs. Yates, Kiely, Komes and O'Connell — direct operations as a whole and each division and department is sponsored by one or another of them.

Formation of this top group may have seemed like a departure from previous patterns but it was, in fact, the means of giving greater emphasis to the traditional Bechtel practice of counselling between the chief executive and his senior associates. Further, through sponsorship responsibilities, it provided close coordination of all company activities and kept channels of communication open in this fast-moving business where prompt, reliable intelligence is basic.

Headquarters and Area Offices

In the 1960's fully staffed offices were maintained in San Francisco and five other U. S. cities — Los Angeles, New York, Washington, D. C., Houston and Lakeland (Florida). Canadian offices were in Toronto, Montreal and Vancouver; overseas activities centered in London, Paris, The Hague and Melbourne. There were long-term project offices in many other parts of the world.

Company policy, as well as economic and political considerations, required that area offices in each country be manned to the maximum by nationals, so the overseas personnel (and to an increasing extent, the domestic) had become truly international. This was considered appropriate for an organization serving a growing number of foreign clients.

Wellman-Lord, Inc.

During the 1960's there was an increase worldwide in the demand for chemical fertilizers, particularly for use in the developing countries. No problem is more pressing than the alleviation of hunger by the rapid and continuous expansion of food production. The company moved quickly into the forefront of this situation as a designer-manager-constructor of fertilizer plants.

To supplement its own resources in this field, Bechtel acquired ownership of a prominent specialized engineer-constructor, Wellman-Lord, Inc., of Lakeland, Florida, which became a subsidiary. Located in one of the world's largest concentrations of phosphates, W-L had completed numerous mines and processing plants and was credited with important innovations in fertilizer plant design.

The acquisition brought W-L's president, James M. Wellman, into the Bechtel organization as a vice president. A proven organizer and businessman, he was a prime force in bringing his 15-year-old organization to an eminent position in its specialty.

Seven Projects Worth $1.7 Billions

As mentioned, Bechtel's growth rate in the 1960's was substantially greater than ever before. The extent to which the organization increased its capacity and capabilities is exemplified by seven large projects which together had a total value of $1.7 billions, individually ranging from $100 millions to $700 millions.

In addition to indicating the rapid acceleration of world economies, these projects showed that risk capital was becoming more and more international. In each case, they were undertaken for consortiums of interests originating in more than one country. The seven projects are, respectively, three pipeline systems, three mining and processing complexes (two for metals, one for oil sands) and a hydroelectric development, as briefly described below.

The South European Pipeline

Connecting the Mediterranean Sea with the upper Rhineland, the South European pipeline was the biggest to grow out of Bechtel's Trans-European pipeline study. This 465-mile system was engineered and managed jointly with French associates in 1961-'62 and expanded in 1965. Expansion to a daily capacity of 600,000 barrels was necessary to satisfy market demands originally forecast to occur five to seven years later. The South European pipeline shortened the average tanker trip from North Africa and the Middle East by five days, lowered transportation costs on the continent and created a major refining center in the Alsace-Upper Rhine area.

Gasunie — Vast Natural Gas Transmission System

Four years after the huge Groningen gas reserves of Northeast Holland were discovered, the Netherlands Government and two interna-

South European Pipeline: multiple lines crossing Lavera harbor, near Marseille, France.

tional oil companies banded together to construct Western Europe's first large natural gas pipeline system. The program's initial phase, carried out between 1964 and 1967, involved 700 miles of main line and feeder pipelines. In a country with 4000 navigable waterways, where much of the land is below sea level and saturation occurs three feet under the surface, pipelaying was extremely difficult. Bechtel's experience and ingenuity were severely taxed but proved equal to the task. The importance to Western Europe's future of the great natural gas reserves in the North Sea and its coastal lands, and their prompt development as pioneered by Gasunie, can scarcely be overestimated.

Transalpine — Mountain-Climbing 3-Nation Oil Pipeline

Certainly the most spectacular of European pipelines is the Transalpine — nearly 300 miles of 40-inch — carrying crude oil from the Gulf of Trieste over the Alps to Central Bavaria. Strategic Transalpine follows a direct route and effects important savings in oil transportation costs. Completed in 1967, initially capable of handling 500,000 barrels per day and designed for expansion to more than a million, this mountain pipeline reaches elevations of nearly one mile. Three tunnels, each over four miles long, obviate the necessity of climbing to higher Alpine passes. Five pumping plants and four relief stations are necessary to get the oil over the grades. Bechtel was responsible for the feasibility study, project engineering, procurement and construction management.

Great Canadian Oil Sands — Sub-Arctic Oil Mine and Recovery Plant

The first of the three mining-processing projects is absolutely unique — one of a kind. It is a "petroleum mine" and refinery in the upper reaches of Western Canada. In this region of Alberta lies what may be the world's greatest reservoir of oil, twice as large as all known conventional sources put together. But the oil, in bitumen-like form, is firmly imprisoned in sand.

Granted the first commercial franchise by Province authorities, the client in a four-year effort has developed portions of a six-square-mile site to mine, extract and refine the raw product into a high-grade synthetic crude oil for transportation by pipeline to the Edmonton pipeline grid. In this pioneering situation the owner has demonstrated the fore-

Through the Austrian Alps—the 40-inch-diameter Transalpine Pipeline, completed in 1967, carries tanker-delivered crude oil nearly 300 miles from Trieste into the heart of industrial Bavaria.

sight, courage and confidence of the true entrepreneur, with tremendously important long-term implications for the entire petroleum industry.

Bechtel reported on feasibility; designed, built and operated a test facility; and handled the subsequent development on a turn-key basis. Commercial operation began in 1967. The complex includes an open pit mine with huge bucket-wheel excavators able to dig 100,000 tons of raw material daily, a high-speed conveyor system, an extraction plant, process units capable of producing 45,000 barrels per day of synthetic crude oil, a tank farm, a 250-mile pipeline, a 20-mile road and a multi-million dollar bridge.

Palabora — Copper and By-Products in South Africa

In February, 1966, a hill in the Transvaal about 250 miles northeast of Johannesburg became one of the largest open pit copper mines in the world. In 1990 the hill will be gone, replaced by the same mine, then 1000 feet deep, a half mile wide and a mile long. This is the Palabora project, which developed copper sulfide deposits estimated at 315 million tons and considered capable of yielding copper with a 1967 market value of more than $2 billions. In addition, Palabora is a major source of magnetite, an iron oxide used in steelmaking, and as a smelter by-product, of sulfuric acid sold for fertilizer manufacture.

The project was designed and managed in a three-year program by a Bechtel-sponsored joint venture, and delivered to its owner several months ahead of schedule. Major project components were the mine, processing facilities capable of producing 80,000 tons per year of copper anodes, an iron concentrate plant, sulfuric acid facilities, a concrete dam, reservoir and some 20 miles of underground pipelines.

In 1967 the joint venture received substantial new contracts for additional facilities and major engineering studies, preliminary to the further expansion of copper production and the development of other minerals and raw materials.

Mt. Newman — Opening Australia's Iron Ore Reserves

In the Spring of 1967 the government of Western Australia authorized an international consortium headed by Australian interests to

Great Canadian Oil Sands Project, Alberta, pioneer commercial development of the world's largest known source of petroleum.

Oil mine: bucket-wheel excavators scoop up 150 tons of tar sand per minute, feed belt wagon and fast-moving conveyor belt to primary extraction plant.

Four highly interested Bechtelites on dedication day, Sept. 30, 1967, at the oil sands project were Jim Brady, manager of refinery and chemical construction; Basil Ince, project construction manager; S. D. Bechtel; and Norman Deiglmeier, project manager.

Fred E. Ressegieu, project manager (center), greeted John Kiely and S. D. Bechtel when they arrived in Labrador to attend ground breaking ceremonies for the massive Churchill Falls hydroelectric development.

proceed with the development of one of the greatest of all known iron ore reserves. The deposit is estimated to contain more than one billion long tons of high-grade iron ore, averaging about 64 per cent iron hematite. Located in the Mt. Newman area, the project comprises an open pit mine, ore crushing and handling equipment, a 270-mile railroad to a port on the Indian Ocean about 900 air miles north of Perth, a pier and extensive harbor works, roads, communications facilities, power plants, airports and townsites.

As with the Orinoco project some 15 years earlier involving work of similar scope, the owners chose Bechtel to manage construction. With 15-billion tons of iron ore believed to rest in the Western Australian hills, the Mt. Newman project and three or four others were expected to shift Australia's prime export from wool to iron ore.

Churchill Falls — Gigantic Hydroelectric Project

Each of the foregoing six projects is, in its field, a pacesetter. Few would have been thought possible of successful realization even a decade or two ago, certainly not in the same magnitude nor with such broadly shared international ownership. Yet the seventh — one of the most ambitious privately sponsored ventures ever undertaken — is still bigger in size and scope.

The international British Newfoundland Corporation (known as Brinco) holds timber, mineral and waterpower concessions in a vast area of Labrador. The most valuable of these rights is that permitting power development of the Churchill River, a mighty stream draining an immense basin, which is calculated to have a power potential of approximately 50 billion kilowatt-hours per year. Nearly two-thirds of this potential is packed into the Churchill Falls area at the edge of the basin.

Bechtel and a Canadian associate have been performing engineering and construction management since 1965 on a long-term hydroelectric project at this site. The eventual installed capacity will be 5.25 million kilowatts from 11 generating units. Earth dikes, rather than a high dam, are planned to create a chain of lakes covering an area 2700 square miles, nearly half the size of Lake Ontario. Arrangements for final financing have yet to be completed by the client.

Capacity and Competence at Record Levels

Several other large projects were also under way. Two publicly owned and financed jobs were described earlier, the San Francisco Bay Area Rapid Transit system and the Wells Hydrocombine — the dam and power plant on the Columbia River in Washington. When these two are added to the foregoing seven projects the combined value of the nine developments is nearly $3 billions. In addition, by late 1967 there were a dozen other major jobs in progress, ranging from $120-to-$220 millions, a fact that further illustrates the continuing growth in project magnitude and duration.

While these figures also reflect the size and volume of the Bechtel business in the 1960's, the resulting revenues are spread over a number of years from the inception to the conclusion of the various projects. Also, it should be noted that despite its activity on such huge undertakings, the company continues to give close and careful attention to many smaller jobs in its chosen fields, and is prepared to handle them economically.

Nuclear Power Comes of Age

Bechtel's continuous involvement in nuclear power over nearly two decades was generously rewarded in the 1960's. By the end of 1967 the organization had completed or was then at work on 27 nuclear-fueled generating units with an aggregate capacity in excess of 14 million kilowatts. Illustrating the sudden acceleration in orders for this type of plant, the figures show that more than 90 per cent of the company's total was in the engineering and construction stages in 1967. In addition, Bechtel conducted studies and furnished consulting services on a number of other nuclear power plants, both domestic and foreign.

How quickly the power utilities decided that nuclear power had become attractive is revealed by this fact: as of January 1, 1965 all U. S. nuclear power plants in operation had a total combined capacity of only 1.2 million kilowatts whereas just one of Bechtel's plants on order in 1967 (Peach Bottom units 2 and 3) alone will generate 2.1 million kilowatts. During the two years, 1966-'67, the American power utilities contracted with manufacturers for some 40 million kilowatts in new nuclear power units, representing nearly half of all new generating capacity authorized in that period.

Since its completion in 1966 the Palabora mining complex in South Africa has become one of the world's leading sources of copper. The molten metal is cast into anodes at the rate of 80,000 tons per year.

The significance of these events was noted by Steve Jr. "These orders," he said, "constitute substantial evidence of the validity of early predictions that by this time nuclear power would be an important factor in decisions to install new capacity. It gives more credibility to the statement that nuclear plants will comprise better than one-third of the world's total electric generating capacity by the end of the century."

Steel: Oxygen Furnaces and Continuous Casting

In the 1960's, as well, major technological advances were being made in one of the oldest basic industries — steel. Bechtel, long an engineer-constructor of steel forming and finishing mills and active for more than ten years on open pit mines and iron ore beneficiation plants, now spread into primary steelmaking facilities. Some involved relatively new processes, such as basic oxygen steel production, vacuum degassing and continuous casting.

With these processes molten steel is rapidly and efficiently produced in basic oxygen furnaces, passed through high vacuum to remove accumulated gases and then continuously cast into solid slab form, ready for the hot mill. Compared with older methods the total process results in a higher quality product and affords numerous economies. Continuous casting bypasses several steps used in conventional production, thus eliminating some heavy capital expenditures. Operating costs are reduced and the yield of usable steel is increased substantially.

These important advantages were combined in a connected series of operations at a new major West Virginia steel mill. Construction began in late 1965. The project was watched with keen interest by the steel industry as the first high-tonnage plant of such advanced design.

Solids to Market by Pipeline

There was bright promise in yet another Bechtel field — pipelines. An iron ore slurry pipeline completed by the company in Tasmania during 1967 may well be the forerunner of many, in situations where they can provide economic outlets for minerals and other valuable solids hitherto locked-in at inaccessible locations or subject to high rates in other forms of transportation.

Slurry pipelines are not new. Under select conditions several have

138

On the Pacific shore some 60 miles south of Los Angeles, San Onofre Nuclear Generating Station's 450,000-kilowatt capability can satisfy the electric power needs of a half million people.

been constructed and given limited use. Now that slurry pipelines have been proved technically feasible and reliable in performance — developments in which Bechtel engineers have been very active — this method of transporting solids is expected to greatly increase in favor.

The project in Tasmania was designed and built to transport 2¼ million long tons per year of iron ore concentrates from a beneficiation plant near the mine to a pelletizer on the coast. In its execution the engineer-constructor encountered numerous construction difficulties. The terrain is mountainous, cut by deep gorges and heavily overlaid with dense rain forests. Trees grow 200 feet high, have diameters up to 30 feet, and the undergrowth is so thick and tough that machetes are useless.

"In addition it was like building a railroad," said its veteran Bechtel superintendent. "For the whole 53 miles the grades could not exceed 10 per cent."

Considering that the pipeline starts at an elevation of 1200 feet, rises another 450 feet and then drops to sea level, maintaining grades of 10 per cent or less was a problem not only of construction but of route siting. Helicopters and bulldozers became essential surveyor's gear. Then — as construction began — torrential rains, including one stretch of 28 days without let-up, brought the job to a halt.

Work resumed at the first possible moment and continued through to completion, including construction of two overhead river crossings of 400 and 1000 feet respectively. Today iron ore concentrates, ground as fine as talcum powder and mixed into a slurry, move profitably to market through formerly impenetrable wilderness by means of the world's first long-distance iron ore pipeline.

Greater Technical Sophistication

During the 1960's the well-established types of work — pipelines, power stations, hydro projects, oil refineries, chemical plants, industrial plants and so on — continued to account for the major part of revenues. But Bechtel was also broadening into new activities.

Assignments were becoming more sophisticated, calling for greater breadth and depth of scientific knowledge and higher order economics. Even sociology was involved in one of the new pursuits—urban planning.

A planned community in Southern California. Bechtel developed the original master plan, did detailed design of the "Park Neighborhood" (above and at right) and designed and constructed the dam.

Model of man-made Bolsa Island off the Southern California coast with world's largest sea water desalting plant and associated nuclear power stations.

Designing for People

Climaxing 70 years of diversified planning, a further expansion of operations assumed substantial proportions under the inclusive title of urban planning and development. This service encompasses everything needed for residential, business or industrial centers, from site location to the preparation of master plans, detailed designs, and the management of entire community developments.

Notable projects include a new city designed for an eventual population of 70,000 and a model town for 4000 people, both in Southern California; deluxe marinas and waterfront residential communities in the Bahamas and Spain; a hillside center for 20,000 residents near San Francisco; site selection studies for the University of California; a petrochemical complex in Holland; a framework plan for development of the 47-square-mile Northern New Jersey Meadows across the Hudson River from Manhattan; and the siting of future facilities at Air Force properties in California and Tennessee. In this time of public concern with land use, the necessity for competent master planning becomes continually more evident. Bechtel created its urban planning-management organization to meet this need, another case of selective expansion into a new growth field.

Salt Water Conversion

Population expansion, industrialization and dwindling natural water resources have spurred increasing concern with saline water conversion and waste water treatment, technical areas in which the company has completed definitive studies and projects for the Office of Saline Water, the Atomic Energy Commission and industrial clients.

Of major importance, Bechtel conducted a comprehensive study for the Metropolitan Water District of Southern California which led to a $440-million project combining nuclear power and the world's largest desalting plant, having ultimate capacities up to 150 million gallons per day of potable fresh water and over 1.6 million kilowatts of power. The study was followed in the fall of 1967 by an early step in realization — the company's selection as designer of the desalting plant, its associated facilities and of a man-made island in the Pacific Ocean on which the plant will be located. Again, as in the case of the Churchill Falls hydro-

143

electric project, arrangements for final financing were under way.

It may well be that no project of these times will prove more significant than the great MWD desalting project, the world's first truly massive program for salt water conversion and the potential trail blazer in solving the problem of vastly expanding the supplies of fresh water available to areas of heavy population density.

Pioneer Applications of Advanced Technologies

In the 1960's also, the company became active in energy conversion. Projects were undertaken in electromagnetics, as exemplified by an 88-inch cyclotron for Texas A & M University. Cryogenic and high-vacuum techniques have been applied to several projects, among them five space simulation and rocket engine testing facilities. Capabilities were being readied for participation in other advanced concepts.

One of the most important fields attracting Bechtel's close attention is pollution control, both of air and water. In addition to conducting studies for the U. S. Public Health Service and for municipal and industrial clients, the company, as an adjunct to large oil, gas, chemical and metallurgical processing plants, has designed and constructed a range of extensive treatment and abatement facilities.

Clean Air — at a Profit

An interesting recent development in the control of air pollution is a new chemical process designed for industrial and power plants by Bechtel's alert subsidiary, Wellman-Lord, Inc. The aim is not only to virtually eliminate contaminants from stack gases but in so doing, to recover sulfur dioxide in sufficient quantities to provide an attractive return on the investment. Continuous recovery of sulfur dioxide from flue gas exceeds 90 per cent and the equipment is adaptable to all types of plants having combustion effluents rich in sulfur compounds. Thus, in addition to permitting the use of low-cost fuels with high sulfur content, this ingenious process (known as Beckwell) is expected to contribute to the presently short supply of sulfur.

Conceived in 1966, the design was proved feasible by the successful operation for five months of a pilot plant built with the cooperation of a Florida power utility at one of its generating stations.

The method, which is relatively simple, involves a chemical absorbent. The sulfur dioxide is recovered as an anhydrous product of very high purity. By putting smog control on a pay-out basis, the Beckwell Process holds great promise for accelerating the reduction of air pollution caused by industrial and power plant emissions.

Fifty Beale Street, San Francisco

To long-time members of this business family no single event better demonstrated the company's maturity than construction of its own home office building in San Francisco. The decision was not made lightly. For two generations, management's philosophy had reflected an opinion widely held in the contracting industry—namely, that working quarters should be kept prudently flexible to accommodate upward and (especially) downward swings in workload. The result: leased quarters. During the 1950's when the new business curve rose steadily, serious consideration was given to a headquarters building. But it remained for Steve Jr. to crystallize the thinking of his associates and take action.

Construction began in April 1966, on property acquired during the preceding year. The home office was then operating at 14 separate locations and these grew to 20 before the new building was occupied early in 1968. For salient reasons of economy, communications, efficiency and convenience the consolidated headquarters office had become a necessity.

Known as the Fifty Beale Street Building, the 23-story structure is located at Mission and Beale, adjoining the city's financial and business center. In choosing the site, major weight was assigned to the residential distribution of Bechtel personnel and accessibility to public transportation, as well as to land cost and the character of the area's future development. The building contains 725,000 square feet gross of floor space, making it one of the most spacious in San Francisco.

Eastward the outlook is to the big Bay Bridge and across the harbor to the mainland shore; southward to the industrial section and the waterfront; westward and to the north into the new skyrise office structures shaping a new profile for the old city. Massive, smartly attractive, businesslike above all — bronze-toned Fifty Beale Street is a fitting world headquarters building for an international engineering, construction and management organization.

Bigness Not the Goal

As noted, that elusive but properly descriptive term "level of effort" had attained quite remarkable heights in the late 1960's. Under the new order, the steps taken by the company's third generation president to strengthen organization proved timely and well planned, for the demands on Bechtel had multiplied many times over. Behind success had to be some great strides in staffing and coordination.

On the other hand, bigness for its own sake was never a Bechtel goal. A study on this subject completed in 1966 by a task force of vice presidents and senior managers concluded that management's prime duty was to provide proper balance between size and creative life for the organization. The task force recognized dangers and defined them. It also cited advantages, identifying these for clients: diversity, depth, ability to handle emergencies, stability and general competence. And for employees: stability, diversity and broadening opportunities. The principal task, the report found, was to furnish the supportive environment that stimulates innovation, growth, accomplishment and self-renewal.

What the Future Will Bring

At a company service award dinner in 1966, S. D. Bechtel was asked to comment on the future outlook. Although then a time of some uncertainty in the business world — the growth rate of the economy was slowing down — Steve spoke confidently, drawing on his long experience.

"Our clients," he said, "include the ranking companies in a range of basic industries. The scope of our service is broad. Our competitive condition is continually being strengthened.

"Furthermore, growth in worldwide developments has made feasible projects of much greater magnitude, some lasting ten years or more.

"Tremendous opportunities lie ahead. Every major industry is being profoundly affected by scientific advance and technological change. Demands are greater than capacity in many lines of business. New plants are urgently needed. Older plants must give way to facilities utilizing improved techniques and processes to attain greater efficiencies.

"In summary, the outlook has never been brighter, particularly for members of a team which has demonstrated its special qualifications for the most difficult and technically sophisticated responsibilities."

Fifty Beale Street, San Francisco, world headquarters of the Bechtel organization.

Keeping Pace with Change

Engineering and construction have become infinitely more complex in the past ten years. Major changes have come with great speed, adding a new dimension to the Bechtel organization's responsibilities and prompting Steve Jr. to alert his people to the necessity of keeping current.

"Obsolescence is the process of going out of use," he said. "The rapid increase in new technology and new business management techniques accelerates this process and presents us with some of the most vexing and challenging problems faced by the engineering and construction industry today.

"In recent years the life cycle of a new idea has been shortened to such a degree that it is now clear that the most successful organizations in our business will be the ones that can most accurately and efficiently assimilate new information, convert it to practical use and pass on the benefits to clients as quickly and effectively as possible.

"The need to adjust to change is not new to us, since as a company we have a long tradition of adapting to changing circumstances. What is new is the rate and extent of these changes.

"To be most effective today implies an awareness of future trends, the direction of change and the preparation of our company resources in advance of actual need."

The Past and the Future

Thus, in the spirit of their predecessors, Bechtel's chief executive and his associates kept their eyes ahead. "You can't run on momentum very long in this business," Steve Jr. told an interviewer from a business magazine, "if you try to base your future on your past it gets away from you pretty fast."

In similar vein, twenty years ago on the 50th anniversary of the business, it was said of the Bechtels:

"Their preoccupation with the present and future showed how they looked at the past — chiefly as an opportunity for building on experience. Use it fully, add to it and go on from there. No job has been done so well that the next cannot be done better."

Certainly that was the case with Bechtel in its 70th year.

CHAPTER EIGHT

Evolution

Over its lifetime, particularly the last 40 years or so under the second and third generations, the development of the Bechtel business has followed a consistent pattern — a steady evolution both of its organization and involvement with certain types of projects.

In transportation the company has traveled a long path from the early railroad construction jobs to super-modern urban rapid transit systems.

In pipelines the start in water projects was followed by local petroleum and natural gas lines, then by national and international pipeline systems, and more recently, by slurry pipelines for iron ore and other solids.

In oil refining, Bechtel projects have advanced from small units with simple flow sheets to extremely large, completely integrated grass-roots refineries utilizing highly sophisticated processes, equipment and control, including automation.

In chemicals and related industries, growth has been from modest, single product plants to massive, computerized multiple-purpose complexes.

In power the spread has been from relatively minor hydroelectric powerhouses to major hydro systems serving large populations; from small steam-turbine generators to gigantic central stations of two million kilowatts or more; from the experimental reactor that first produced nuclear-energized electric power to present-day plants of great size and efficiency, often computerized; and over-all, from hydro to steam to nuclear power.

In mining and metallurgy Bechtel's progress has been from mine stripping and ore production to the latest technologies of metals recovery and ore beneficiation; and in steel from local forming and finishing mills to prime steelmaking plants utilizing such advanced processes as basic oxygen melting and continuous casting.

In desalting — only now meeting its long anticipated destiny — the company's experience paces the state of the art, from the small thermal units of 20 years ago to great nuclear-powered salt water conversion projects, able to supply the water and power needs of major industrial complexes, towns and even cities, with unprecedented economies.

In community planning, work began with layout and operation of the railroad and Hoover Dam construction camps, followed by temporary and permanent towns adjacent to remote projects — as at Dhahran and Little Aden — later expanded to include urban master planning and the development of industrial parks, residential and business centers, and entire new cities.

In human terms, the evolution has been from a family group with a few employees to a worldwide professional organization with a hard core staff of 12,000 engineers, managers and constructors — including some 6000 in technical classifications.

Truly a remarkable progression!

But these are results, not causes. Behind Bechtel's evolution are men — the Bechtels themselves and their senior associates primarily, the management organization and others at all levels, especially professional people and the seasoned builders in the field, doing their jobs the world over.

"This kind of evolution," the senior Steve says, "is possible only where there is real continuity of philosophy and objectives, strong traditions and a consuming dedication to continuous improvement."

Board of Directors, Bechtel Corporation, September 1967. Seated, from left: J. F. O'Connell, J. R. Kiely, J. P. Yates, S. D. Bechtel, S. D. Bechtel Jr., K. K. Bechtel, R. L. Bridges and J. W. Komes. Standing: E. J. Garbarini, R. A. Bowman, I. R. Caraco, C. T. Draney, R. D. Grammater, E. Lippa, W. S. Slusser.

Epilog

For the last thirty years Bob Ingram has had a place in the Bechtel Business Family held by few others.

Several years ago we invited him to write of an important era in the company's development.

A few months ago he asked me to review a draft of this volume, *The Bechtel Story*. It is primarily a history of the last two decades. With the exception of a few suggestions of emphasis and the supplying of a few facts, this book is the result of his thought and effort. To the best of my knowledge it is correct, although some of us oldtimers shine more prominently in the present-day sun than may be factual.

Since working in railroad camps in the summers of 1914 and 1915 — except for the time taken out for education and military service during World War I — I have been privileged to be one of a group of men who, some say, have helped to bring about constructive changes in various parts of the world. While there have been stormy periods, we have always kept the ship headed into the wind and have ridden out the storms. More often than not, we have had following winds.

As time went on, and particularly since Steve came into the home office as an officer, then president, it was gratifying to reflect on the past — to take real pride in what is being done today — but even more thrilling to contemplate the new fields yet to be plowed.

I wholeheartedly thank all with whom I have shared the early development of our organization and enthusiastically applaud those who are carrying on. Many in both groups have been mentioned in these pages but many more whose names do not appear because of space limitations have also helped greatly in furthering our growth and effectiveness. They will understand that their contributions are well recognized and deeply appreciated.

This is the story of our organization's activities and development. However, it should always be remembered that without the enthusiastic and effective support of our wives and families the organization would not have developed as it has nor would its spirit be what it is today.

Particularly I wish to gratefully acknowledge the loyalty and cooperation given by the fine people of my staff. Over the years their assistance has been of inestimable value to me and to our whole organization.

It is a pleasure to add this epilog to *The Bechtel Story*.

SAN FRANCISCO   STEPHEN D. BECHTEL
APRIL 1968

Appendix

Directors of Bechtel Corporation
From Incorporation September 10, 1945 Through
December 31, 1967

Active Directors		*Past Directors*	
S. D. Bechtel	1945 –	J. K. Doolan	1945-1955
S. D. Bechtel, Jr.	1951 –	V. G. Hindmarsh	1945-1953
K. K. Bechtel	1945 –	J. A. McCone	1945-1946
J. P. Yates	1945 –	V. W. Rosendahl	1945-1953
R. L. Bridges	1947 –	J. L. Simpson	1945-1961
J. R. Kiely	1954 –	W. E. Waste	1945-1967
J. W. Komes	1955 –	John Byrne	1947-1953
R. D. Grammater	1960 –	G. S. Colley, Jr.	1947-1958
J. F. O'Connell	1960 –	J. M. Rogers	1947-1955
C. T. Draney	1961 –	C. S. Snodgrass	1947-1952
E. J. Garbarini	1964 –	G. E. Walling	1947-1953
Eugene Lippa	1964 –	S. M. Blair	1957-1967
W. S. Slusser	1965 –		
R. A. Bowman	1967 –		
I. R. Caraco	1967 –		

The Directors' Advisory Group

Formed in 1964, this group consists of the vice presidents of Bechtel Corporation and selected members of senior management who serve actively for specified terms. Both as individuals and members of DAG these men — many with long and distinguished service records — are key contributors to the Bechtel organization's competence and success. Including vice presidents, those who are or have been members since the inception of DAG are:

S. M. Akeyson, Jr.
G. B. Arnold
W. E. Arthur
W. L. Bass
P. G. Behr
R. A. Bowman
J. F. Brady
H. W. Brown
G. L. Bruno
H. F. Brush
G. E. Buchanan
J. P. Buehler
W. A. Bugge
D. W. Campbell
P. W. Cane
I. R. Caraco
R. A. Cheatham
R. M. Collins
J. H. Crispin
W. L. Daniels
W. K. Davis
M. de Simo
A. Dor
R. M. Dorman
D. R. Ferguson
S. B. Ford
S. P. Giambra
R. P. Godwin
J. H. Goodell

R. F. Grambow
J. Griffen, Jr.
M. E. Harper
C. F. Hochgesang
J. H. Jackson
L. J. Kelly
J. N. Landis
J. M. Leaver
E. C. Lee
C. B. Lester
I. Leviant
M. G. Lewis
J. Lindenbaum
M. M. Loewenthal
D. M. Logan
J. F. Lynch
R. C. Lynn
E. J. Mahoney, Jr.
R. E. May, Jr.
M. M. McGarraugh
J. W. Merryman
F. W. Meyer
R. E. Miller
T. W. Moran
W. H. Ness
A. J. O'Donnell
J. J. O'Donnell
A. J. Orselli
J. G. Patrick
F. D. Perry

J. H. Poulson
C. Rankin
H. O. Reinsch
F. E. Ressegieu
D. Rhodes
M. J. Rosenthal
W. M. Sanders
G. W. Saul
J. S. Sides
R. H. Simmonds
W. S. Slusser
C. E. Slyngstad
R. L. Stater
C. D. Statton
J. D. Stubbs
K. O. Taylor
P. E. Thompson
W. H. Thompson
J. G. Thon
M. Van Hoesen
R. L. Walker
H. F. Waste
G. L. Way
J. M. Wellman
C. E. White
S. V. White
B. F. Willson
K. G. Wolfe
A. P. Yates

PHOTOGRAPHS: JON BRENNEIS, FRONTISPIECE; DENNIS BOWMAN, 60, 63; COMMONWEALTH EDISON CO., 83; CONSUMERS POWER CO., 95B; HERBERT BRUCE CROSS, 141; FAY FOTO SERVICE, 115B; RICHARD FINNIE/BECHTEL, 27, 29B, 30, 32, 39A, 51, 56B, 56C, 81, 87, 88B,88C, 97, 107A, 129, 134B; RAYMOND FRAYNE/BECHTEL, 147; JOERN GERDTS, 25B; H. H. HALL, 29A; RAY HASSMAN, 55A; WILL HAYS, 15, 92; WILLIAM HEICK/BECHTEL, 39B, 59, 70, 74C, 84, 101B, 107B, 108, 131, 133, 134A, 137, 139, 151; HERB JACK/BECHTEL, 25C, 47B, 52, 55B, 55C, 67C, 74A, 74B, 102; J. R. KIELY, 47A; RICHARD KOCH, 142; JACK MCMINN/MCGRAW-HILL, 77, 101A; PHILADELPHIA ELECTRIC CO., 95A; PURDUE UNIVERSITY, 115C. DESIGN BY GEORGE MCWILLIAMS